clapping and shouting can bring you back. Ever.
enough to conjure your flesh back inside the skin.. RSS
It's already happened. So turn the volume down
— ED PAVLIC

#11 Conversations with Poets who
Refuse to Speak

Thanks to:
PRINCE CLAUS FUND
PAN AFRICAN MARKET
MC FOND AFRICA CENTRE
ALL CONTRIBUTORS

chimurenga (ISSN#1683-6162) is a project of
the Kalakuta Trust (IT642/2005)

www.chimurenga.co.za

Greetings Mr. PREZ

On the cusp of the old into the New Year I received a mandate from the children and adults living in the Jozi inner city and immediate environs. The equivalent of 3 days 'n nights I walked with a calling and strength from our ancestors. The first time I was sent was on a Wednesday morning @ 2am. I walked from Yeoville to Hillbrow. First stop: a place designed for the car herd - disused during the night, it is run by a woman not older than 12 or 13 years.

I have as currency in my bag a smidgin of ganja, about 4 rands, toiletpaper, grapevine cards and a pen & koki. Oh, and Alice Walker's *Living by the Word*.

So here is this group of adolescents. I go in, place my butt in her circle, intro myself. They've already seen me enter, it's at least a 7m walk to the inner periphery where she and her boyz are blomming (males are mainly older, perhaps up to 17 yrs). They've had enuff time to scope me and decide on response. I have very little to say beyond introduction. She's burning the tar. A controlled fire. Sy manage die hele ding. My eyes crisscross this fairly huge carpark. Clusters of boys all over. Clearly mutual protection is in action. There's a deference to her as young female providing fire inventively & maintaining her poise in a scenario that screams stereotype: that whole collocation of rape, abuse, mutilation, theft and this and that bullshite.

Sit for a while. Watching. Listening. Occasional interjection. Not liberalistic about the fact that this is a virgin or a victim, on the streets everything is currency, but really it's how you maintain dignity in transaction that matters.

They are ok. I give thanks, greet, leave. Walk a couple of blocks. Find myself up from the Huguenot Hotel where my friend Gypsy lives, one of the women who taught me to reclaim my talent for walking these night hrs & space without fear. Leave a msg with her friend, peroxide blonde.

Move on. Up towards Pretoria street. Find a group of boys - varying ages - from about 8 to 17. Hectic concentration on a street game of chance. Feel emboldened to engage more directly. Hallo, ek is hier, howzit, are you ok? Can I ask you some stuff? No real answer, just degrees of what kind looks. So, if I were to write a letter to Mr Thabo Mbeki tomorrow, because I'm a writer and have to use my skill, what shall I say you guys say? The littlest of the coons, does a jack-in-the- box. *We want your poes*. Haikona. What's wrong with you? You're so tiny, you have sexual feelings, go around the corner and wank. I am your mother, die poes van jou ma. You come from me and in my natural order I don't fuck little boys of eight. Has your environment warped you so much that the only way you can see me is through a sex prism. I can give you love & food and some understanding and that's about it, so let's recheck. Tatamachance game arrested for a moment, the group heaves in laughing appreciation.

Ok so bottleneck bullshite unclogged for a precious momento.

Older, very beautiful eyes, direct gaze, young man says: *so you're serious*. Like, ja.
In 3 phrases and 11 seconds he sums it up: *the churches and the shelters are doing very good work with us. What we need is extras. More food, more blankets, some books and art materials and stuff like that.*

Mr President I took a train from Cape

Town to Jozi on 3rd class @ R190 a seat to assist a female friend of mine. A music exec producer, we did UWC together 20 years ago when Jakes Gerwel was resident principal, she had just had her fourth child on 22 October 05, Mandla, and was given 5-day notice by some UK privileged person of minor melanin to vacate her space. A 3wk old baby, Mr Mbeki, and the H20 WAS CUT immediately after the vacation notice. With her Zim-born steeldrum maker and musician husband in Qatar, finally on a paying gig until beginning January 06, she calls for back-up.

Arrive in Yeoville, we sort out - no money as currency - her moving. She goes with 4-person brood to an artist space for 2 wks. Arrive, the books are dusty, the art hangs awry. Remove *Thus spoke Zarathustra*, leave it at Xoliswa's space who has no compunction about putting together groceries for the two families I will be spending the next number of weeks with. One the mother and children; two, the place where I am squatting id est artists park, the burnt-out house in the cul-de-sac of Wyndcliff avenue, just beneath the water tower. It is here that I return at 5.30am after Hillbrow sojourn. Now at this house, there are mainly musicians and Jah people - you occupy a space, you rebuild and make habitable. While I am there, I harangue the whole yard to plant spinach (having gifted them with a pkt of seeds) saying, *if you plant now, you have your first crop in Jan/Feb*. As in any social organism,

human development is irregular: while some yardies are industrious and inventive, some have succumbed to a toxic cocktail of ennui, excessive consumption of African beer and/or hard drugs and hopelessness. The room that I am in has three double-beds, on any given evening there are between 8 and eleven people sleeping. Gooftroep the head honcho, has not only constructed a corrugated iron ceiling, but has established engineering and aesthetic mastery by providing a skylight (an open section where the tin slabs meet) so that you are in constant commune with the rain, thunder, sun and stars; yet never get wet. At the same time, it reduces the horrendous impact of the fly population residing there because of the rubbish heaps that have not been removed. This too becomes a daily battle: I organise refuse removal bags, a spade and hope to get the men on the yard to start cleaning up. In the event this starts slowly, until I lose patience and instruct the children to make art out of the rubbish and install their works in front of the house. Anyway, Gooftroep charges males R10 per night for a bed and a cooked meal. Females pay in kind - cook, do washing, look pretty and sexy, keep the room clean and generally maintain some kind of moral order. Sexual transactions are private.

Back from Hillbrow, a plate of food awaits. I've given up meat - Imperative: Don't eat what you can't kill - so I remove the flesh and eat the spinach and pap that Lerato has prepared, at the same time providing the requisite report back to whoever is the assembled crew. Next move - no sleep while others weep - about 4 hours later. Market Theatre. Am working with culture activists on the artists' programme of 16 days of activism over 365 days against violence against women and children to be launched on the last Friday of November. Am there for 3 days working with the artists to make paper cut-out figurines depicting male abuse. Just before I have to leave for the Market Theatre, Lerato informs me that we're out of water. The closest point is the garage past Rockey st. If you want to fill a 5 litre: 7 min walk without water, if you're a strong 21 yr old female with one other, 25 minutes with a full container. I go, no no, don't have time, I'll go opposite to fellow hack and arts editoress, flat owner, she'll give us a bit of water for body washing and making breakfast. She says no. I'm like, you know what, if men are abusing women and children we are all complicit, we have all

3

Hooui ll
—Tsakau

allowed the social compact to slipslide - all adults of the human species irrespective of gender. Am saying, I cannot enter the 21stC with this kind of equivocation. Let us all take responsibility for the madness and move on 'n beyond. Imperative: Rape is instruction of fear. Imperative: Adult males and females abuse their children to prepare them for their environment. As it is, as you like it, Gail's gardener opens the side gate and allows me in. He fills the 5-litre with H20. He takes me to the swimming pool at the back and lets me breathe with him for a while. Says: *Sister, breathe in breathe out.*

Am thinking, fuck this. I will walk the change. Imperative: I want to witness your words coincide with your deeds. Imperative: H20 is not conditional. Imperative: Energy is not optional. Imperative: Change is not a choice.

SO I WALK. This time, DAG 2, the ancestral void moves me to the Mandela bridge. Bare feet. Move over there at high noon. Pulsating car thugs, wie is djy. Towncrier. Ek huil op die brug. Move on, Market Theatre. Arrive. 1st stop, the entrance of the theatre leading to Moyo's. Burn Mphephu. Security. Avoid that punitive stuff successfully. Can avoid that stuff successfully because the market of people outside the Market has already shown them up. Check: sleek cowhorn earrings and necklaces; check the ethiopian kings with soft bridal cheesecloth to enclose the strident body of queen; check: regal bronze children in bas relief for the hearth or the throat; and everywhere, tourists.

SEE Mr president, on DAG 1, I took a slight walk from the former site of the photographic workshop (now the space of 16 days over 365 days of…) to the growing arts and crafts market in the Mary Fitzgerald Square & went bos because my people had assumed their artistry; gone super-refined. As I exclaimed, in thanks at the overcoming, a line of white sheep trundled past. One had a camera with zoom in function, caught my exclamation of joy. I react: you did not ask my permission. Would it not be interesting to be a native rather than a tourist on your planet. Since you have captured my image, I expect payment for it. You are sitting in front of lavish tables laden with food that the 40 of you will never be able to consume in one meal and I don't have water. Please pay me for my picture.

Security is called, I evade arrest with the admonitory question: what are you securing and the caveat; do not touch me without warrant. I leave, but the next day, return to burn our traditional cleansing herb.

From the Market precinct to Yeoville, where I've resided intermittently for eleven years, the last year of that period as fully fledged itinerant of no fixed abode. Now, Mr President, here the young and not-so-young people are very kinky and astute. They live, literally, by their wits and an ironic embrace of the hustle. Nobody cares that you hustle, just do it with some style and a high resolution entertainment gloss. Here, I meet up with the skarrelaars every morning and we write the day's news in whatever form with whatever resources are available. I move with the day's gedagtes which generally find resting and cognition point at the Basement at the end of the day, where the young come to boogie to hardcore goema drum 'n bass, reggae, ragga and stylish house, hip hop & kwaito. I'm training them to dance when the tanks come. All year, the law enforcers have been instigating unruly behaviour with absurd curfews and raids and shows of force with SWAT teams and laser guns. I had warned the head of the local police that we are too smart to give them an L.A. riot scenario irrespective of their provocation and the local councillor's and JDA's disrespect and inaction (and possibly corruption) on the urban renewal programme. Usually all this action theory is framed by Andrew B who will just go on a 24-hour philosophical rampage and locate the whole inversion from a dom darkie POV. That's one constituency.

Most of the rest of the hood operates, like the 70% of urban slumdwellers across the globe, via an informal economy. What needs to be bought is sold: simple. You can get a plated meal of pap/rice with chicken/beef and a vegetable for R10-R15. More often than not, that plate is shared with 2 or three others. The most expensive cooked meal is R20 and that's ok because the Central and West Africans members of the community serve a mean fish plate while the East Africans provide a R15-R20 smorgasbord of delicacies served with their local bread, injeera, that can easily fill four stomachs. Beer quarts come between R7 and R8, African beer is anything between 1 rand and 5 rands per skaal while the Zimbabwean imported cigarettes go for 50 cents. If you have a home you can, at the lowest end of the economic spectrum feed 9 people 3 times a day on approximately R20 - that would be tea, bread, pap, chomole or cabbage and a bit of meat/ chicken necks/ kidneys or lungs for the evening meal. Most people factor in fresh fruit and eggs too. Same principle of local trade operates with clothing, goat & cow smileys, hairdressing, furniture, live chickens, art works, internet cafes, telecommunications and so forth. Here people are taking over abandoned buildings and making them habitable. There's a shebeen in one Yeoville street that had me struck dumb early last year. So packed with families that the foyer to the house had a double-bed that housed 5 schoolgoing children and 2 adults. When I returned in December; the place had been almost entirely renovated (with additions of outside rooms and toilets) and the inside rooms had been regulated. Spaces that are not rooms are partitioned by curtains and cloths and respect for privacy is maintained. At the same time, everyone resident has one key to the front door. All this instigated by and sustained by the magogos and females of varying ages who make their living brewing and selling African beer.

So basically Mr President, the second economy *is* the first economy. In this space and elsewhere in the country. Now, I can not afford easy assessments. But, having returned to my mother city, I find that in Mitchell's Plain, that urban sprawl of perceived dislocation; besides the chemical enquirers and the ones primed as cannon fodder; the laaties (I don't regard adults too seriously @ the moment) are clued-up about the global and local state of play. It's a wired, anti-war, supersmart, anti-excess generation. These young ones - Biko's spawn - are not so much unaware as they are waiting for adults to provide some kind of wise leadership and discernment. Our job really, is to provide moral and philosophical foundations. Be the ultimate semiotician.

DAG 3. Back to the Market Theatre.
Day of the launch of 16/365-days-of-activism-against-violence-against-women-and-children.
I take myself away for the afternoon and walk to Hillbrow where I go and give respect to the peeps blomming behind the communal toilets, then off to Harlequin's pub where I spend 2 hours counselling a Yeoville resident whose daughter is dying of cancer as well as writing imperatives artistically, as my central contribution to the messaging for

the launch. Return to Market Theatre where we start transforming the art workshop space into the launch site. I give 2 pieces of paper to 2 children and ask them to make something. One of the banners we've made proclaims: CUT OUT CHILD ABUSE. I ask the young boy what he is making - *a spine* - the young girl is making *a snake*. I take these two pieces and arrange them like flowers so that the banner reads both as CUT OUT CHILD ABUSE and as CUT OUT ABUSE. At this stage two of the males (white males) with this project interject and start ripping it apart. I object. Argument: this messaging is tired. Every adult is complicit in a social contract that breeds greed, violence and poverty. Let us all mea culpa and let us all, male and female and child start instituting a workable alternative. *No, No,* they cry and forcibly remove me from the site. As I am ejected, I witness Prof Keorapetse Kgotsitsile and photographer Cedric Nunn witness the ejection. Nunn invites me to his exhibition upstairs. I stay for 5 minutes and eject myself.

Walk up Bree street, past the taxi rank, through an alley bordering Home Affairs. Just beyond, I come across rows and rows of blanketed bodies. Go up to our people, greet with handshakes and start talking to everyone row by row. Is this ok. You are not going to lose it, are you. What do you need to sustain. Every single one of the close to 100 people sleeping there, has a smile and a quip. *No No, everything is alright. We just need to make more of a living. We survive OK, it's quite fun some times. No No, we're not interested in Violence, Elections, No No, we are not going to vote. We just need to make more work and more food.*

I am a woman walking alone, so Karel is designated to escort me home. Up from the Windybrow Theatre as you ascend the winding hill into Hillbrow, there is a disused car park. *Kom*, Karel says, *let me show you something*. Ek is ook nie lui nie. Down we slither a hill of rubbish. Every single entrance to this place, with the exception of one, is composed of years and years of compacted rubbish. There are people living there. Karel motions me to a corner, which I can see leads to the main road. I follow. Just before the fence is a shitcovered cloth. He throws me onto it, pins me down with his weight. Asks for sex. No. How can I make a rational decision if I cannot breathe. If you force me it's rape. So what are you going to do. You were so cool, walking with me and showing me how our people are surviving and now what do you think I must take back with me. Think man THINK. You are a real man, you are oulik, I love sex, but I also want to have a choice about it, you know. Hiatus. He releases me. I get up and shake Karel's hand, thank him, say goodbye and move on.

Eject yourself

Be the ultimate Semiotician

Co-Conspire

Mr President, you are president to a nation of nations that is characterised by cool and analytical thinkers. The diaspora stops here. Everywhere is home. The only ones who are excessive are those who already have. Those who don't have possess remarkable restraint. Do not expect much from this round of municipal elections. As the man at the shebeen under construction says, your government is *in breach of contract*. As award-winning filmmaker Xoliswa Sithole says, your and Mr Mugabe's biggest joint failure is *failure to deliver and invest in human capital*. People want back-up, the edifice and the walls of the house are being built. You've given us the vote, you've given us a bit of magic space globally to manoeuvre and come up with a workable plan. We are getting there. Drop the falsehood of the 1st economy, take your cue from the remarkable, resilient nations of people who reside here and let's deliver for the world what your compatriot Steven Bantu Biko had prophesied: that Africa's greatest gift to the world yet needs to come and that is to give it a human face. Let's breathe together. Co-conspire. Ubuntu is here. Zen it - Be a Bee.

Respect and courage

chim peeps.

Gael Reagon is a writer living in Cape Town and Jozi. She is contributing editor at *Chimurenga*. Photographs by Tsakane Maubane from the *Hoeville* series.

Quiet Encroachment Of The Ordinary

A traveller to Middle Eastern cities, Tehran, Cairo or Rabat cannot help observing the peculiar ways in which poor children stroll in the streets to sell their products, women occupying public spaces of the sidewalk to market vegetables or fruits, and thousands of men having turned public thoroughfares into brisk and busy bazaars. The traveller cannot escape noticing gangs of informal car parkers who control the main streets, turning them into their own private gains with, at times, elaborate organisation and division of labour. Often pavements are filled with private business sites, stalls, kiosks or simply street restaurants. Perhaps the more dramatic are the sites of public lands invaded by squatters, or those wherein illegal constructions are erected on legal lands. Between twenty to fifty percent of city spaces, or city escapes, are taken over and "developed" in such a manner. Admittedly, this movement is not limited to Middle Eastern cities. One finds similar patterns from Rio de Janeiro to Jakarta. How do we explain this appropriation of public space for private gain? As scholars have already noted, this has a lot to do with the way in which the poor people work in developing countries. It has to do with the life exigencies of the urban disenfranchised in the global South, especially when confronted by the structures of economic and political forces in their societies. It has to do with the "low politics" of the poor.

Some have viewed this as poor people's "survival strategies," or "urban social movements," or lower class "resistance." Here, I would like to assess the issue from a different angle, in terms of the quiet encroachment of the ordinary. The notion of "quiet encroachment" describes the silent, protracted but pervasive advancement of the ordinary people on the propertied and powerful in order to survive and improve their lives. They are marked by quiet,

largely atomised and prolonged mobilisation with episodic collective action - open and fleeting struggles without clear leadership, ideology or structured organisation. While the quiet encroachment cannot be considered a social movement as such, it is also distinct from survival strategies or "everyday resistance" in that, first, the struggles and gains of the agents are not at the cost of fellow poor or themselves, but of the state, the rich and the powerful. Thus, in order to light their shelter, the urban poor tap electricity not from their neighbours, but from the municipal power poles; or to raise their living standard, they would not prevent their children from attending school in order to work, but rather squeeze the timing of their formal job, in order to carry on their secondary work in the informal sector.

In addition, these struggles are seen not necessarily as defensive merely in the realm of resistance, but cumulatively encroaching, meaning that the actors tend to expand their space by winning new positions to move on. This quiet and gradual grassroots activism tends to contest many fundamental aspects of the state prerogatives, including the meaning of order, control of public space, of public and private goods, and the relevance of modernity.

I am referring to the lifelong struggles of the floating social clusters - the migrants, refugees, unemployed, under-employed, squatters, street vendors, street children and other marginalised groups, whose growth has been accelerated by the process of economic globalisation. I have in mind the long processes in which millions of men and women embark on long migratory journeys, scattering in remote and often alien environs, acquiring work, shelter, land and living amenities. The rural migrants encroach on the cities and their collective consumption, the refugees and international migrants on host states and their provisions, the squatters on public and private lands or ready-made homes, and the unemployed, as street subsistent workers, on the pubic space and business opportunity created by shopkeepers. And all of them tend to challenge the notions of order, the modern city and urban governance espoused by the Third World political elites.

The concrete forms of encroachments vary considerably. Post-revolutionary Iran saw an unprecedented colonisation, mostly by the poor, of public and private urban land, apartments, hotels, street sidewalks and public utilities. Between 1980 and 1992, despite the government's opposition, the land area of Tehran expanded from 200 square kilometres to 600; and well over a hundred mostly informal communities were created in and around Greater Tehran. The actors of the massive informal economy extended beyond the typical marginal poor to include the new "lumpen middle class," the educated salary-earners whose public sector position rapidly declined during the 1980s. In a more dramatic case, millions of rural migrants, the urban poor and the middle-class poor have quietly claimed cemeteries, rooftops and state/public lands on the outskirts of Cairo, creating well over a hundred spontaneous communities which house over five million people. Once settled, encroachments still continue in many directions. Against formal terms and conditions, the residents then add rooms, balconies and extra space in and on buildings. Those who have formally been given housing in public projects built by the state illegally redesign and rearrange their space to suit their needs, by erecting partitions and by adding and inventing new space. Often whole communities emerge as a result of intense, daily struggles and negotiations between the poor and the authorities and elites.

The encroachers force the authorities to extend urban services to their neighbourhoods by otherwise tapping them illegally and using them free of charge. Once utilities are installed many simply refuse to pay for their use. Some forty percent of poor residents of Hayy al-Saloum, a south Beirut informal community, refuse to pay their electricity bills. The cost of unpaid water charge in the Egyptian city of Alexandria amounts to $3 million a year. Similar stories are reported in urban Chile and South Africa where the poor have periodically refused to pay for urban public services after struggling to acquire them, often against the authorities' will. Hundreds of thousands of street vendors in Cairo, Istanbul and Tehran have occupied the streets in the main commercial centres, infringing on favourable business opportunities the shopkeepers have generated. Thousands of inhabitants in these cities subsist on tips from parking cars in streets which they control and organise in such elaborate ways as to create maximum parking space. Finally, as in many Third World cities such as those in South Korea, the encroachment of the street vendors on copyrights of labels and trademarks has caused invariable protests from the multinational companies.

As the state employees and professionals, the previously privileged segments of the workforce, feel the crunch of neo-liberal policies, they too resort to their own repertoires of quiet encroachment. To compensate for the meagre $40 monthly salary, the school teachers in Egypt turn to private paid tutoring of their own pupils. By doing so, they have created a massive sector of illegal private teaching which generates some $2 billion a year, costing at least 25 percent of the annual earning of Egyptian families. Similarly, the street lawyers or "unregistered practitioners," who do not hold law degrees, but have acquired some legal knowledge by working as employees in law offices, encroach on the legal profession. They then share their legal experience with the new law graduates (who cannot afford high cost of establishing law offices) to offer competitive services.

These actors do not carry out their activities as a deliberate political act; rather, they are driven by the force of necessity - the necessity to survive and improve their lives. Necessity is the notion that justifies their often unlawful acts as moral and even "natural" ways to maintain a life with dignity. Yet, these very simple and seemingly mundane practices tend to shift them into the realm of contentious politics. The contenders get engaged in collective action and see their actions and themselves as political only when they are confronted by those who threaten their gains. Hence a key attribute of the quiet encroachment is that while advances are made quietly, individually and gradually, the defence of their gains are often, although not always, collective and audible.

Driven by the force of necessity (effects of economic restructuring, agricultural failure, physical hardship, war and displacement) they set out their ventures individually, often organised around kinship and friendship ties, and without much clamour. They even deliberately avoid collective effort, large scale operation, commotion and publicity. At times the squatters, for instance, prevent others from joining them in specific areas; and vendors discourage their counterparts to settle in the same vicinity. Many even hesitate to share information about their strategies of acquiring urban services with similar groups. Yet as these seemingly desperate individuals and families pursue similar paths, their sheer cumulative scores eventually turn them into a social force.

But why individual, quiet and direct action, instead of collective demand-making? Unlike the factory workers, students or professionals, these people represent groups in flux, operating largely outside institutional mechanisms through which they could express grievance and enforce demands. They lack an organisational power of disruption - the possibility of going on strike, for example. They may participate in street demonstrations or riots as part of an expression of popular discontent, but only when these methods enjoy a reasonable currency and legitimacy (as in Iran immediately after the revolution, Beirut during the civil war, or after the fall of Suharto in Indonesia in 1998), and when they are mobilised by outside leaders. Thus, urban land takeovers may be led by left-wing activists; and the unemployed and street vendors may be invited to form unions (as in Iran after the revolution, in Lima or in India). This, however, is uncommon, since more often than not mobilisation for collective demand-making is prevented by political repression in many developing countries where these struggles often take place. Consequently, in place of protest or publicity, these groups move directly to fulfil their needs by themselves, albeit individually and discretely. In short, theirs is not a politics of protest, but of redress - a struggle for an immediate outcome through individual direct action.

What do these men and women aim for? They seem to pursue two *major* goals. The first is the *redistribution of social goods* and opportunities in the form of the (unlawful and direct) acquisition of collective consumption (land, shelter, piped water, electricity, roads), public space (street pavements, intersections, street parking places), opportunities (favourable business conditions, locations, labels, licenses), and other life chances essential for survival and acceptable standards.

The other goal is *attaining autonomy*, both cultural and political, from the regulations, institutions and discipline imposed by the state and modern institutions. In a quest for an informal life, the marginals tend to function as much as possible outside the boundaries of the state and modern bureaucratic institutions, basing their relationships on reciprocity, trust and negotiation rather than on the modern notions of individual self-interest, fixed rules and contracts. They may opt for jobs in self-employed activities rather than working under the authority of the modern workplace; resort to informal dispute resolution rather than reporting to police; get married through local informal procedures (in the Muslim Middle East under local Sheikhs) rather than by governmental offices; borrow money from informal credit associations rather than banks. This is so not because these people are essentially non- or anti-modern, but because the conditions of their existence compel them to seek a mode of life outside modernity. Modernity is a costly existence; not everyone can afford to be modern. It requires the capacity to conform to the types of behaviour and lifestyles (adherence to strict structures of time, space, contract and so on) which most vulnerable people simply cannot afford.

But how far can the urban subaltern exercise this autonomy? Not only do the poor seek autonomy, they also need security from state surveillance because an informal life in the conditions of modernity is also an insecure life. Street vendors may feel free from the discipline of modern working institutions, but they suffer from police harassment for lacking business permits. The struggle of the poor to consolidate their communities, attain schools, clinics or sewerage would inevitably integrate them into the prevailing systems of power (i.e., the state and modern bureaucratic institutions) which they wish to avoid. In their quest for security, the urban marginals are therefore in constant negotiation and vacillation between autonomy and integration. Yet, they continue to pursue autonomy in any possible space available within the integrating structures and processes.

Becoming Political

If the encroachment begins with little political meaning attached to it, if illegal acts are often justified on moral grounds, then how does it turn into a collective political struggle? So long as the actors carry on without being confronted seriously by any authority, they are likely to treat their advance as an ordinary, everyday exercise. However, once their gains are

threatened, they tend to become conscious of the value of their doings and gains, defending them often in collective and audible fashion, as shown by the mobilisation of squatters in Tehran in 1976, of street vendors in the 1980s, and the street riots of squatters in several cities in the early 1990s.

Alternatively, the actors may retain their gains through quiet non-compliance without necessarily engaging in resistance. Instead of collectively standing by their businesses, the mobile street vendors in Cairo or Istanbul simply retreat into the back streets once the municipal police arrive, but immediately resume their work as soon as the police are gone. At any rate, the struggles against the authorities are not about winning a gain, but primarily about defending and furthering gains already won.

The states' position vis-à-vis this type of activism is affected, first, by the extent of their capacity to exercise surveillance, and, second, by the dual nature of the quiet encroachment (infringing on property, power and privilege, and, simultaneously, being a self-help activity). Third World states seem to be more tolerant of quiet encroachment than industrialised countries where similar activities, albeit very limited, also take place. The industrial states are far better equipped with ideological, technological and institutional apparatuses for applying surveillance over their populations. In other words, people have more room for autonomy under the vulnerable and "soft" states of the South than in industrialised countries, where tax evasion, infringement on private property and encroachment on the state domains are considered serious offences. On the other hand, quiet encroachment may in many ways benefit the Third World governments for it is a mechanism through which the poor come to help themselves. It is no surprise then that these governments often express contradictory reactions toward these kinds of activities. The soft states, especially at times of crises, tend in practice to allow the encroachments when the latter still appear limited. For their part, the encroachers attempt constantly to appear limited and tolerable while, in fact, expanding. They do so by resorting to tactical retreats, going invisible, bribing the officials, or concentrating on particular and less strategic spaces (for instance, squatting in remote areas or vending in less visible locations).

However, once their real expansion and impact is revealed or when the cumulative growth of the actors and their doings pass beyond a tolerable point, the state crackdown becomes expectable. Yet in most cases, the regulations fail to yield much result, since they are launched usually too late when the encroachers have passed the point of no return. Indeed, the official descriptions of these processes as "cancerous" brings home the dynamics of such movements.

The sources of conflict between the actors and the state are not difficult to determine. First, the distribution of public goods free-of-charge exerts heavy pressure on the resources which the state controls. Besides, the rich - the real-estate owners, merchants and shopkeepers - also lose properties, brands and business opportunities. The alliance of the state and the propertied groups adds a class dimension to the conflict. Secondly, the quest for autonomy in everyday life creates a serious void in the domination of the modern state. Autonomous life renders the modern states, in particular the populist versions, rather irrelevant. Moreover, autonomy and informality (of agents, activities, and spaces) deprive the states of the necessary knowledge to exert surveillance. Unregulated jobs, unregistered peoples and places, nameless streets and alleyways, and policeless neighbourhoods mean that these entities remain hidden from the governments' books. To be able to control, the state needs to make them transparent. Indeed, government programs of squatter upgrading may be seen as strategies of opening up the unknown in order to be able to control it.

Nowhere is this conflict more evident than the streets, this public space par excellence. The streets serve as the only locus of collective expression for, but by no means

limited to, those who generally lack an institutional setting to express discontent, such as squatters, the unemployed, the street subsistence workers, street children, members of the underworld and housewives. Whereas factory workers or college students, for instance, may cause disruption by going on strikes, the unemployed or street vendors can voice grievances only in the public spaces, the streets. Indeed for many of these disenfranchised, the streets are the main, perhaps the only, place where they can perform their daily functions - to assemble, make friends, earn a living, spend their leisure time and express discontent. Streets are also the public places where the state has the most evident presence, which is expressed in police patrol, traffic regulations and spatial divisions - in short, public ordering. The power relationship between the encroachers and the authorities is what I have termed "street politics."

Two key factors render the streets an arena of politics. First is the use of public space as a site of contestation between the actors and the authorities. In this sense, what makes the streets a political site is the active or participative (as opposed to passive) use of public space. This is so because these sites (sidewalks, public parks, intersections, etc.) are increasingly becoming the domain of the state power which regulates their use, making them "orderly." It expects the users to operate them passively. An *active use* challenges the authority of the state and those social groups that benefit from such order.

The second element shaping street politics is the operation of a *passive network* among the people who use and operate in the public space - an instantaneous communication among atomised individuals which is established by a tacit recognition of their common identity, and which is mediated through space. Vendors of a street are most likely to recognise one another even if they never meet or talk. Now when a threat occurs to the vendors in the street, they are likely to get together even if they do not know each other or have not

active use + passive network = active communicate
when the shit hits.

planned to do so in advance. The significance of this concept lies in the possibility of imagining the mobilisation of atomised individuals, such as the quiet encroachers, who are *largely* deprived of organisations and deliberate networking. The street as a public space has this intrinsic feature that makes it possible for people to get mobilised through establishing passive networks. Once the individual actors, the encroachers, are confronted by a threat, their passive network is likely to turn into active communication and cooperation. Thus an eviction threat or police raid may immediately bring together squatters, or street vendors, who even did not know one another. Of course, the shift from passive network to collective resistance is never a given. Actors might feel that tactical retreat would yield far better results than confrontation, a tendency so common in Cairo's streets today, but uncommon in revolutionary Iran where on-the-spot collective resistance prevailed.

Conclusions

A major consequence of the new global restructuring has been a double process of integration, on the one hand, and social exclusion and informalisation, on the other. Both processes tend to generate discontent on the part of many urban grassroots in the Third World.

First, there are many among the urban grassroots who find it difficult to function, live and work, within the modernising economic and cultural systems characterised by market discipline, contract, exchange value, speed and bureaucracy, including the state organisations. These people attempt to exit from such social and economic arrangements, seeking alternative and more familiar, or informal, institutions and relations. Secondly, globalisation has also a tendency to informalise through the programs of structural adjustment, rendering many people unemployed or pushing them to seek refuge in the informal production, trade, housing and transportation. Transnational street vendors (circulating, for instance, between the new Central Asian

Republics and Istanbul, or between Jamaica and Miami) are the latest product of this age. In short, the new global restructuring tends to intensify the growth of subjectivities, social space and the terrain of political struggles that are coming to characterise the cities of the developing world.

Although the prevailing perspectives (survival strategy, urban social movements and everyday resistance) provide useful angles to view the activism of the urban subaltern, they do, however, suffer from major drawbacks. The latter are reflected in the essentialism of the "passive poor," the reductionism of "surviving poor," the Latino-centrism of "political poor" and the conceptual perplexity of "resistance literature." I suggest that the "quiet encroachment" perspective might offer a way out of those conceptual problems. Looking from this vantage point, the poor struggle not only for survival, but strive in a lifelong process to improve their lot through often individualistic and quiet encroachment on public goods and on the power and property of the elite groups. In this process, the grassroots do not directly challenge the effects of globalisation. Rather, in their quest for security, they get involved in constant negotiations with globalisation to maintain or seek autonomy in any space that has remained unaffected. At the same time, in this process the unintended consequences of their daily encroachments and negotiations beget significant social changes in urban structure and processes, in demography and in public policy. Yet the question remains as to how far this quiet encroachment can take these actors? Given their existential constraints (poor skill and education, or meagre income, connection and organisation) the quiet encroachment serves as a viable enabling strategy for the marginalised groups to survive and better their lot. However, this non-movement is neither able to cause broader political transformation, nor does it aim to do so. The larger national movements have the capacity for such transformation. Yet, compared to global/national mobilisation, these localised struggles are both *meaningful* and *manageable* for the actors—meaningful in that they can make sense of the purpose and have an idea about the consequences of these actions; and manageable in that *they*, rather than some remote national leaders, set the agenda, project the aims and control the outcome. In this sense for the poor, the local is privileged over the global or national.

It is true that the disenfranchised succeed relatively in extending their life-chances, often through lifetime struggles; nevertheless, crucial social spaces remain out of their control. The marginals may be able to take over a plot of land to build shelters, may tap running water or electricity illegally from the main street or neighbours;

they may secure a job on the street corner by selling things and may be able to bribe or dodge the municipal police every now and then. But how can they get schools, health services, public parks, paved roads and security - the social goods which are tied to larger structures and processes, the national states and global economy? In other words, the largely atomistic and idealist strategies of the disenfranchised, despite their own advantages, leave a search for social justice in the broader, national sense poorly served. The urban grassroots are unlikely to become a more effective player in a larger sense unless they become mobilised on a collective

basis, and their struggles are linked to broader social movements and civil society organisations. Yet, it is crucial to remember that until this is realised and its result is tested, quiet encroachment remains a most viable enabling strategy, which the urban grassroots pursue irrespective of what social scientists think of it.

Despite the bland assertions of sociologists, high visibility actually rendered one UN-VISIBLE — Ralph Ellison

taught sociology and Middle East studies at the American University in Cairo. He is currently Academic Director of the International Institute for the Study of Islam in the Modern World (ISIM).

52 NIGGERS

Julius Eastman had a way of walking. He had a swagger, a way of swinging hips. He rarely strolled or ran. Instead, skin tight jeans/ black leathers slung low on his waist, sucked down by the velocity of his gait, he cruised and rolled. He played loose. He played cool. He worked fast.

He scored *Stay on It* in one sitting. He wrote through the night, the full next day, the next night. He wrote fast. He wrote moment, place. He wrote sentiment and soul. He orchestrated the body: his body, body in motion, body as it flexes to move a pen, form a fist, make mark, lift a drink.

He rewrote the classical music canon. He inserted pop. He noted free improvisation. He bucked the conventions. He fucked minimalism. He reworked the rulebook: Cage's anal atonal progressions, Glass' linear additive processes, Reich's phasing and block additive methods. He started the Post Minimalist revolution, New Music, Improvisation, call it whatever you like.

He made the call. He beat them all to it: John Cage, Steve Reich, Philip Glass. This was 1973. This was America. Glass was still only glistening on the surface. Reich was outside the country, hauled up somewhere in Africa, playing poacher, plundering Ghanian polyrhythmic beats. Cage was still stuck in his cage, his soundproof room, his anechoic chamber. Cage was still tuning silence; tuning into his nervous system in operation, low throb of his blood in circulation. Cage was tuning: "Until we die there will be sounds."

Who needs them? Eastman was already at the edge. While Cage could only hear his body, Eastman's music mapped those sounds: pulses pounding, sweat producing, blood surging in veins. While Reich filched, Eastman felched, digging his tongue deep, exposing himself, getting off on his own shit. Fuck the division between private and public, feral cruise and cocktail soirée. Fuck stuffy formalism of avant-garde composition: "forms", "malls", "isms" and restrictions.

"He had radar that could detect bullshit." He hated that shit. He hated hip hyp-o-crazy: the lecture halls, the concert chamber; the sound proofed rooms and white gallery cubes. Everything purged of colour. Specifically: all the walls and the ceilings and the floors; white. More white than white, the kind of white that repels. No smells, no noise, no colour; no doubt and no dirt. No nothing. No eating, no drinking, no pissing, no shitting, no sucking, no fucking.

He rebelled. He headed out. He hit the gay clubs, the crack houses, disco dens. He listened up to the sound on the street. He saw the violence. He saw the hate. He saw anger. It moved him. It ran him. It called his shots. He stayed cool with it. He stayed justified. He channelled the rage. He wrote it down. He stayed on It; He spread the word. He said: "Find presented a work of art, in your name, full of honour, integrity, and boundless courage."

It was futile. They ignored him. They indulged him. They used him. They strung him along. A black face looked good on record. 1974.

The Creative Associates on the bench of the Albright-Knox Gallery. Official photograph. Used by permission. Front, l-r: Julius Eastman. His features a blur, the white balance thrown out - shooting for white - just a duffle coat and sneakers, just an outline, a black smudge, a dark mark, stop gap framed by smiling white faces.

They used him to fill the gaps. Petr Kotik looked him up. He was putting together a concert series. Big names: John Cage, Earle Brown, and Christian Wolff, the original New York School. They wanted to diversify. They were looking for someone to represent. Kotik wooed him. Kotik went through the motions. Kotik invited him around. Uptown apartment. Konik at the door. He said, "Come in. Straight through here." He pointed with his hand. He led the way. He said, "Grab a seat." Eastman sat. Eastman stared. Fancy pad: white walls, plants and lights, stiff long-back chair. Konik poured drinks. Konik smiled. Konik paid lip service. "What kind of music do you want to hear? You hungry?"

He said, "Big Break." He said, "Big names: John Cage, Earle Brown, Christian Wolff." Eastman sat, stared. Eastman listened. Eastman timed the pause. He felt the hate. He felt the anger. He started to say - No, wait. Maybe? He took a breath. He challenged the rage. He counted notes. He took the score. He said, "Sure Pete!" He sat. He smiled. He had this craaazy idea.

The performance took place. 1975. The June in Buffalo Festival, SUNY Buffalo. Now legendary. Now infamous. Kyle Gale told and retold the story: "Chaotic at best! Eastman performed the segment of Cage's *Songbooks* that was merely the instruction, 'Give a lecture.' Never shy about his gayness, Eastman lectured on sex, with a young man and woman as volunteers. He undressed the young man onstage, and attempted to undress the woman..."

He started with her top button. He worked fast. He worked fastidiously. His hands jumped. He dripped sweat. Second button, third. She wasn't sure. She trembled. She shut her eyes. Fourth button. The audience twittered. The audience buzzed. She looked up. She made eye contact. Her eyes swam. She grabbed his hand. Everything froze. Time hung back. She looked down. She broke free. The audiences erupted. The audience roared. Someone stormed the stage. Someone hit the lights.

All hell broke loose. John Cage freaked. Cage raged. Was that meant to be a joke? Who's laughing? Am I laughing? He came down hard. He came down spitting words, throwing authority. He said, "I'm tired of people who think that they can do whatever they want with my music!" He stormed. He banged the piano with his fist.

He said, "The freedom in my music does not mean the freedom to be irresponsible!" He used his lecture's voice. He couldn't make the break. For all his talk about crossing boundaries - noise/ music, life/ art - he couldn't take the leap. His "anti-art" was still the same old shit: natural law devalued, social tradition minimized, rebellious gestures only accepted if they stayed safely walled in, caged within the tradition they sought to denied. Cage as cage.

Even his thinking on silence was caged, locked within the audible order, a lecturer's voice: something to learn, rather than lose yourself in. Silence as ambient sound, non-intended sound. Silence as the sounds of life. He said, "Until we die there will be sounds." He said there will only be silence in death. The implication was left hanging: we can't experience our own death so we can't experience silence. Silence, like death was the impossible crossing of a border. Audibility vs. inaudibility, life vs. death: oppositions that can't be overcome, borders that can't be crossed. And the hierarchy was clear: Life was where it was at. Death was the undesirable, a dispensable deviation, something to be silenced.

Caged said, "I have nothing to say and I am saying it." Eastman had something to say and he was unsaying it. Cage raged and lectured. Eastman acted. He showed up the con of Cage's "instructions". He de-con-structed. He gave voice to silence. He injected real life, lived experiences, street politics into art. He created an unsound politico-musical discourse, a line of flight that radically threatened Cage's abstract political discourse, the white language of the classical avant-garde. He scared the shit out of Cage.

Cage reacted. Cage hit back. He said, "Irresponsible!" He rallied support. Walter Zimmermann called it "rotten". Peter Gena said, "Abuse!" Petr Kotik called it "sabotage". He said, "I should have guessed he was unsuitable." He said, "scandal." Eastman was tagged: Crazy Nigger. The reputation stuck. The blacklist built: Eastman the Evil Nigger, Eastman the Savant Saboteur, Gay Guerrilla sooo-preme.

His guitarist brother Gerry said, "Give it up Julius. Play jazz. At least a black man can make half a living playing jazz." Fuck that shit, man. He refused. He knew the score; their story is history: crazy black gay mutherfucker, all danger and despair and downward trajectory. Ismael Reed's old "post-Mailer syndrome", the "Wallflower Order": "Jes Grew, the Something or Other that led Charlie Parker to scale the Everests of the Chord… manic in the artist who would rather do glossolalia than be neat clean or lucid."

He refused to be composed. He answered them with *If You're So Smart, Why Aren't You Rich?* A 20-minute fuck you. Fuck you to your score. Your over-determined definitions of what it means to be black. Pre-de-scribed borders and hierarchies: beginning/end, classical/jazz, silence/sound, white/black, between order/disorder, meaning and meaninglessness, life and death.

He worked on unweaving the whiteness from within. He started at the end, a funeral march, a single line, chromatic scales on slow ascent, going going then BAM! Drawing it up, drawing it out, ripping it open, a quick-draw halt, a slash, a silence, coma, full stop, semicolon connoting rhythm of speech, interrupted thought. Then more scales, building slowing, coalescing, multiplying the metre into a seething swarm, a glowing brass mass where desire equals death, where death, and the approach to human death, is no longer an end but a beginning.

He kept his own score. He rocked up for rehearsals dressed like a jazz cat, a disco queen. All black leather and chains and dripping desire and fuck yous. He pitched high or drunk. He hung loose, he jived, whisky slung low in left hand, a tight fist. Then he hit the piano and everything changed. Time changed. Time redacted. Space erased. Knuckles became fluid, joints broken down, fingertips riding hard and wide; trembling then going taut.

The contradiction was too much. They wrote him out. They wrote him off. They accused him of silencing himself. "He could have had it so good if only he hadn't had the personality problems." He lost his post at SUNY-Buffalo. They called him in. The office. Two chairs. One desk. The books lining the walls like ghosts from another epoch. The Professor shuffled papers. His button down shirt perfect white, white on white. He cleared throat. He glanced up. He said, "Take a seat". He cited, "Neglect of administrative duties." Eastman didn't stay for the rest. He walked. He took the stairs. He said, Paperwork? Fucking paperwork? He didn't know whether to laugh or cry. Outside it was warm. Thirty degrees at noon. Campus was crammed. Students between lectures, taking lunch. They jostled him. They pushed past.

He kept walking. He followed the sound on the street. Downtown, 1980, music pumped from open windows and revved motors, fragments and samples, notes and the repetitions. Richard Pryor's world of "junkies and winos, pool hustlers and prostitutes, women and family" all screaming to be heard.

He wrote hard and fast. He scored *Evil Nigger*, *Gay Guerrilla*, *Crazy Nigger* in close succession. He tore into classical tropes and constructs. He deconstructed. He found rhythm. Street politics embedded in the beat, the repeated piano riffs, the propulsive badbadDUMbadaDUM brass blasts. Cool cadence balanced rhythmic flow, as in poetry, as in the measured beat of movement, as in dancing, as in the rising and falling of music, of the inflections of a voice, modulations and progressions of chords, moving, moving through a point beyond sight, sound, vision, being.

He played the preacher man, rocking out on a counting-in chant, "one-two-three-four". He played the poet. He re-dubbed Lee Perry's "I am the Upsetter. I am what I am, and I am he that I am". He wrote *The Holy Presence of Joan of Arc*. He said, "This one is to those who think they can destroy liberators by acts of treachery, malice and murder." He rapped Richard Pryor's *Supernigger*. He was unstoppable.

He played The Kitchen. He hit the stage alongside Merdith Monk and Peter Gordon. He hooked up with Arthur Russell. He toured Europe. He filled houses. He flew off. He came back. He put out feelers to record. He was ready to get it down. To get it out.

Reich's *Music for 18 Musicians* was going massive. Glass' *Metamorphosis* was everywhere. He contacted cats he knew via the circuit. He said, "What've you got going?" He waited. He made more calls. He chain smoked and watched TV. He slept through whole days. He woke. He drunk whisky. He slept. He watched TV. Old Pryor skits on NBC. "White. Black. Coloured. Redneck. Jungle bunny. Honky! Spade! Honky honky! Nigger! Dead honky. Dead nigger."

He played the college circuit just to keep going. North Western 1980. Members of the faculty took offence. The African American fraternity didn't like the nigger shit. It was like Édouard Glissant never existed. Like Ismael Reed, Richard Pryor, hip-hop never happened. No word on the street. He had to explain. From the beginning. "Recontextualization? You know the whole 're-appropriation', 're-cannibalisation' thing?"

He took to the mic. He said: "There are three pieces on the programme. The first is called *Evil Nigger* and the second is called *Gay Guerrilla* and the third is called *Crazy Nigger*." He spoke smooth. He flowed easy. He mirrored Pryor's buzz in making obscenities sing. He paused after each title. He let it hang. He waited for it: the reaction, breath suspended, waiting for a ripple, a laugh, some kind of recognition of the humour at play. Nothing. Fuck. His audience was silent. Not even a twitter, a nervous giggle. He held the pause a second longer - Jesus, even he felt like laughing - but no, nothing. Just silence, just Eastman, just his nerves' systematic operation, his blood's endless circulation.

He tried again. His voice wavered. His voice woofered. It bounced high and wide. FUCK - Overfeed. Overamp. From the start. He said, "Nigger is that person or thing that attains to a basicness or a fundamentalness, and eschews that which is superficial, or, could we say, *elegant*." He said, "There are 99 names of Allah." He paused. He said, "There are 52 niggers." But still it wouldn't go away. The whiteness always returned, whiteness woven into the fabric of Culture, whiteness locking everything else out. Silent. White faces stared back. Blank, unmoved: they could see only one.

One more drink. One more pill. It was getting tight. 1982. Nothing coming. The walls closed in. Cash was low. The apartment cost. The clubs cost. The drink cost. He got headaches.

He drank himself to sleep. He swallowed whisky shooters. He popped uppers. He shot poppers. A downhill slide. Cornell University turned him down. "He was just too damn outrageous."

A failed application to the Paris Conservatoire. The letter came in the post. One white envelope, black type. He said, "Damn them damn them damn them." He tore it up. He let it drop. He headed out to score. He head east, the lower Eastside. Further out, the windows all covered meshed-over glass burglar proof stuff; homeboys on the sidewalks rhyming beefs, little men with big shirts and the chicks in tight skirts.

He kept going. He walked. He didn't give a shit. He felt zero. He felt zip. He felt ate up. His skin buzzed. He took a left. He crunched glass underfoot. He took a right. Low door. Dark interior. Match boxes and glass pipes. Cracker jacks on low stools. White smoke that hung in low clouds. He took a seat. He took the hit. He sucked deep. He held it in. He let go. He felt it hit. His mouth closed. His head dropped black. His eyes rolled. And white appeared. Absolute white. White beyond all whiteness. White of the coming of white. White without compromise, through exclusion, through total eradication of non-white. Insane, enraged white, screaming with whiteness. Fanatical, furious, riddling the victim. Horrible electric white, implacable, murderous. White in bursts of white. God of "white." No, not a god, a howler monkey. *The end of white.*

[Julius Eastman died in 1990. *Unjust Malaise*, a 3 set CD of his compositions, culled from university archives, was released by New World Records in 2005. This was Eastman's first official release. No commercial recordings of his work were made during his lifetime.]

Stacy Hardy is a writer living in Cape Town.

Ethel Sharrift
(Chicago 1963)

leader of the women's corps of the
Black Muslims / wife of the chief
of the elite guard / daughter of
Elijah Muhammad —

The Cleavers
(Algiers 1970)

Mrs. Jeferson
(Fort Scott 1949)

Mr. PARKS
AKA "Shaft"

Gordan Parks (1912 - 2006) was a photographer, filmmaker, writer and musician.

He didn't like new things. Like a blind man, he preferred stuff he'd used for a long time, even small things like pens or knives, things he'd come to feel at home with.

Walking with him one afternoon, we were waiting for the lights to change at a street corner near his place - we were always near his place. He rested his hand against a lamppost, patting it affectionately:

—My favourite lamppost.

Everyone in the neighbourhood knew him. Walking to the shops, kids called out, Hey, Monk, howya doin? Where ya bin, Monk? and he mumbled something back, stopping to shake hands or just sway back and forth on the sidewalk. He enjoyed being recognized like this - not a fame thing but a way of enlarging his home.

He and Nellie moved into an apartment in the West Sixties and stayed there, with their children, for thirty years. Twice fires forced them to move out and twice they moved back. Most of the space was taken up with a Baby Steinway, jammed halfway into the cooking area as though it were a piece of kitchen equipment. When he played his back was so close to the stove it looked like he might catch fire. Even if he was composing it made no difference what kind of bedlam was going on around him. He'd be working on some really tricky piece with kids crawling in and out of the piano legs, radio playing loud country music, Nellie cooking dinner while he worked away serene as if he was in the cloisters of some old college.

—Nothing made any difference to him, long as no one messed with him or Nellie; didn't care if no one heard his music, long as he was playing it. For six years, after he got busted for possession and lost his cabaret card, that room was practically the only place he did play.

He and Bud Powell were in a car, got pulled over by the police. Bud was the only one with anything on him but he froze, sat there clutching the folded paper of heroin. Monk snatched it from him and sent it butterflying out the window, landing in a puddle and floating there like a little origami yacht.

Monk and Bud sat and watched the red and blue lights from the prowl car helicoptering around them, rain sweating down the white glare of the windshield, the metronome flop of wipers. Bud rigid, holding himself barbed-wire tight. You could hear the sweat coming off him. Monk already ahead of everything, just waiting for it to happen, seeing the rain-black shapes of police lurching toward them in the rearview mirror, keeping his breath steady. A flashlight shined into the car, Monk eased himself out, a puddle clutching at his foot and then flattening itself down again like someone shocked briefly out of sleep.

—What's your name?
—Monk.
—You got ID?

Monk's hand moved toward his pocket…

—Steady, motioned the cop, loving the threat of saying it slow like that.

Handed him a wallet with the cabaret card, the photo on it so dark he could have been anyone. He glanced at Bud in the car, his eyes full of rain and lights.

—Thelonious Sphere Monk. That you?
—Yeah. The word came clear of his mouth like a tooth.
—Big name.

Rain falling into pools of blood neon.

—And who's that in the car?
—Bud Powell.

Taking his time, the cop bent down, picked up the stash of heroin, peered into it, dabbed a little on his tongue.

—This yours?

He looked at Bud, shivering in the car, looked back at the cop.

—This yours or his?

Monk stood there, rain falling around him. Sniffed.

—Then I guess it's yours. The cop took another look at the cabaret card, tossed it like a

< WINNERS HAVE YET TO BE ANNOUNCED >

Most of them play it way too loud. Maybe they've already sold their souls to noise. Make noise out of anything. Fill mountain air with car horns. Up early, jack hammers with toothbrush fittings. Up late, I've seen them hang chimes off sills to keep the wind from sneaking thru the bars on their bedroom windows. Up all night.

Maybe life itself has become a kind of manic noise? Even the quiet's made of noise. White noise. Planned activities. Conversations morphed into guided tours. People keep their brains ready for visitors. Visiting hours. More like open houses than conversations. Want to know where I was a year ago last Tuesday, 2 - 3:30. I'll get my planner…Yep. Like I thought, here it is, 2 - 3:30, nowhere, talking with no one.

cigarette into a puddle.

—And I guess you won't be needing that for a while, Thelonious.

Monk looked down at the rain pattering his photo, a raft in a crimson lake.

Was Monk got busted but he never said nothin. Something like that wouldn't even occur to him, to rat on Bud. He knew what kind of a state Bud was in. Monk was weird, coming and going out of himself like he did, but Bud was a wreck, a junkie, an alcoholic, half the time so crazy he was like a jacket with no one inside it - no way could he have survived prison.

Monk did ninety days, never talked about prison. Nellie visited him, told him she was doing everything she could to get him out but mostly just sat there waiting for him to say something back to her, reading his eyes. After he got out he couldn't play in New York. The idea of ordinary work never entered his mind and by then he'd just about made himself unemployable anyway, so Nellie worked. He made a few records, played out of town a few times but New York was his city and he didn't see why he should have to leave it. Mainly he just stayed at home. Laying dead, he called it.

The un-years was what Nellie called them. They came to an end when he was offered a residency at the 5-Spot for as long as he wanted, as long as people wanted to see him. Nellie came most nights. When she wasn't there he got restless, tense, pausing for an extra-long time between numbers. Sometimes, in the middle of a song, he called home to see how she was, grunting, making noises into the phone that she understood as a tender melody of affection. He'd leave the phone off the hook and go back to the piano so she could hear what he was playing for her, getting up again at the end of the song, putting another coin in:

—Still there, Nellie?
—It's beautiful, Thelonious.
—Yeuh, yeuh. Staring at the phone like he was holding something very ordinary in his hand.

He didn't like to leave his apartment and his words didn't want to leave his mouth. Instead of coming out of his lips the words rolled back into his throat, like a wave rolling back into the sea instead of crashing onto the beach. Swallowed as he spoke, forming words reluctantly as if language were a foreign language. He made no concessions in his music, just waited for the world to understand what he was doing, and it was the same with his speech, he just waited for people to learn to decipher his modulated grunts and whines. A lot of the time he relied on a few words - shit, motherfucker, yah, nawh - but he also liked saying stuff that nobody understood. He loved big words as names for his songs - crepuscule, epistrophy, panonica, misterioso - big words that were joky too, words as difficult to get your tongue around as his music was to get your fingers around.

Some nights he'd give a little speech from the stand, the words lost in brambles of saliva:

—Hey! Butterflies faster than birds? Must be, 'cause with all the birds on the scene in my neighbourhood there's this butterfly and he flies any way he wanna. Yeah. Black-and-yellow butterfly.

He'd started the bebop look of berets and shades but that had become a uniform like the music. When he was playing now he liked to dress in suits as sober as possible, or sports jackets, setting these off with hats that defied logic but which he made look completely ordinary - as though a "mollusc" hat worn by Asian peasants were as essential an accessory to a suit as a collar and tie. Did his hats have any effect on his playing? His face filled with a huge grin:

—Nawh, haha. Well, I dunno. Maybe they do...

Me too, I sing them too loud. But, in my head, they're somewhere beneath whispers. Volume, yes, immense volume, but not loud. Or quiet. It really has nothing to do with amps. Amplitude silent as karst in the fog on rice paper. Majestic, even, the longevity of a wave has its own sounds.

You mean wave length?
You again? Can't you wait outside in the street anymore?
It's raining.
How'd you get in?
Don't worry about that, you were saying?
Since you're so interested, no. I mean

volume. The way a song fills a room. Rooms after rooms. Like real human flesh. Maybe you've heard of it? The way songs build, cloud my head and spill down my arms. Just like with people, as if they've taught my hands things and left me out of it. The way you learn to play music from the inside out. You don't get to know a song by introducing yourself. You can't just walk up on it like this here... There's no guided tour. It won't shake your hand. You have to find an opening.

In the song?

Man, in yourself.

25

When someone else was soloing he got up and did his dance. He started quietly, tapping a foot, clicking his fingers, then he raised his knees and elbows, rotating, shaking his head, meandering everywhere with his arms outstretched. Always looking like he was about to fall over. He spun around and around on the spot and then lurched back to the piano, giddy with purpose. People laughed when he was dancing and that was the most appropriate reaction as he shuffled around like a bear after its first taste of strong alcohol. He was a funny man, his music was funny, and most of what he said was a joke except he didn't say much. His dancing was a way of conducting, finding a way into the music. He had to get inside a piece, till it was a part of him, internalise it, work himself into it like a drill biting into wood. Once he had buried himself in the song, knew it inside out, then he would play all around it, never inside it - but it always had that intimacy, that directness, because he was at the heart of it, he was in it. He didn't play around the tune, he played around himself.

—What is the purpose of your dancing, Mr. Monk? Why do you do it?

—Get tired of sitting at the piano.

You had to see Monk to hear his music properly. The most important instrument in the group - whatever the format - was his body. He didn't play the piano really. His body was his instrument and the piano was just a means of getting the sound out of his body at the rate and in the quantities he wanted. If you blotted out everything except his body you would think he was playing the drums, foot going up and down on the hi-hat, arms reaching over each other. His body fills in all the gaps in the music; without seeing him it always sounds like something's missing but when you see him even piano solos acquire a sound as full as a quartet's. The eye hears what the ear misses.

He could do anything and it seemed right. He'd reach into his pocket for a handkerchief, grab it, and play with just that hand, holding the handkerchief, mopping up notes that had spilled from the keyboard, wipe his face while keeping the melody with the other hand as though playing the piano came as easy to him as blowing his nose.

—Mr. Monk, how do you feel about the eighty-eight keys of the piano. Are they too many or too few?

—Hard enough playing those eighty-eight.

Technically he was a limited player in that there were all sorts of things he couldn't do - but he could do everything he wanted to, he wasn't held back by his technique. Certainly no one else could play his music like he could (if you played the piano properly, there were all sorts of little things you couldn't get at) and to that extent he had better technique than anyone. Equilibrium: he could think of nothing he wanted to do and couldn't.

He played each note as though astonished by the previous one, as though every touch of his fingers on the keyboard was correcting an error and this touch in turn became an error to be corrected and so the tune never quite ended up the way it was meant to. Sometimes the song seemed to have turned inside out or to have been constructed entirely from mistakes. But a logic was operating, a logic unique to Monk: if you always played the least expected note a form would emerge, a negative imprint of what was initially anticipated. You always felt that at the heart of the tune was a beautiful melody that had come out back to front, the wrong way around. Listening to him was like watching someone fidget, you felt uncomfortable until you started doing it too.

Sometimes his hands paused and changed direction in midair. Like he was playing chess, picking up a piece, moving it over the board, hesitating and then executing a different move from the one intended - an audacious move, one that seemed to leave his whole defence in ruins while contributing nothing to his attacking strategy. Until you

③
An open tone in the ache that connects your hands and feet and fingers. Mistakes disappear overnight. Things you never could do appear. Here's the change, but you can't remember paying. Old habits come back full of totally new errors. Closer. Any volume contains constant movement the feeling of getting closer. Illusion: the volume of wonder.

Like the volume of a dream. Immense, full. It's never loud. It's how a sound fills a submerged structure. Underwater bridge. Careful with unannounced changes in register. Broken chords. Chapter after the transitive property of attributes, the sensual nearness of opposites, altitude & depth switch places without warning. Bang. Sweat and a silver prayer. A sperm whale can issue a sonic blast powerful enough to crush the chest cavity of a diver. Pressure increases. Go deep enough, even simple amplitude can get you dead.

Every sound has its afterlife. It comes from somewhere, passes thru on its way. What people call volume, it's their way of trying to stun the sound, the song. It's not music, it's shock therapy. They need to keep it close to where they think they are. Of course, they're wrong. They're not where they are and the anchors they've made of music don't have a bottom to hit. It's why every decent song says, "don't you wish you were here…" but you're not. & you are. It's why every great song says, "welcome, you held on to the chain too damn long." Easy now. Every great song says: "you love somebody… and you have the right to remain, silent."

realised that he'd redefined the game: the idea was to force the other person to win - if you won you lost, if you lost you won. This wasn't whimsical - if you could play like this then the ordinary game became simpler. He'd got bored with playing straight-ahead bebop chess.

Or you can look at it another way.

If Monk had built a bridge he'd have taken away the bits that are considered essential until all that was left were the decorative parts - but somehow he would have made the ornamentation absorb the strength of the supporting spars so it was like everything was built around what wasn't there. It shouldn't have held together but it did and the excitement came from the way that it looked like it might collapse at any moment just as Monk's music always sounded like it might get wrapped up in itself.

That's what stopped it from being whimsical: nothing makes any difference with whimsy, whimsy is for low stakes. Monk was always playing for high stakes. He took risks and there are no risks in whimsy. People think of whimsy as doing whatever you feel like - but there's less to whimsy than that. Monk did whatever he wanted, raised that to the level of an ordering principle with its own demands and its own logic.

—See, jazz always had this thing, having your own sound so all sorts of people who maybe couldn't have made it in other arts - they'd've had their idiosyncrasies ironed out - like if they were writers they'd not 've made it 'cause they couldn't spell or punctuate or painting 'cause they couldn't draw a straight line. Spelling and straight-line stuff don't matter necessarily in jazz, so there's a whole bunch of guys whose stories and thoughts are not like anyone else's who wouldn't've had a chance to express all the ideas and shit they had inside them without jazz. Cats who in any other walk of life wouldn't've made it as bankers or plumbers even: in jazz they could be geniuses, without it they'd've been nothing. Jazz can see things, draw things out of people that painting or writing don't see. *Bullshite!*

He insisted his sidemen play his music the way he wanted but he wasn't dependent on them the way Mingus was. Always it was Monk and the piano, that was really what the music was about. How well they knew

his music mattered more to Monk than whether they were great soloists. His music came so natural to him that it baffled him, the idea that anyone could have trouble playing it. Unless he was demanding something beyond the physical possibilities of the instrument he assumed his sidemen should be able to play whatever he asked.

—Once I complained that the runs he had asked for were impossible.

—You mean they don't give you a chance to breathe?

—No, but...

—Then you can play 'em.

People were always telling him they couldn't play things, but once he gave them a choice - You got an instrument? Well, you wanna play it or throw it away? - they found they could play. He made it seem stupid to be a musician and not be able to do things. Onstage he'd get up in the middle of playing something, walk over to one of the musicians, say something in his ear, sit down again and resume playing, never hurrying, wandering around the stage as his hands wandered around the tune. Everything he did was like that.

One time Hawk and Trane were having trouble reading some of the parts and asked Monk for an explanation.

—You're Coleman Hawkins, right, the man who invented the tenor? And you're John Coltrane, right? The music's in the horn, between you you should be able to work it out.

Most of the time he said little to us about how he wanted us to play. We'd ask him questions two or three times and get no response, he'd be staring straight ahead as if the question were addressed to someone else, to someone else in another language. Made you realise you were asking him questions and you knew the answers all the time.

—Which of these notes should I hit?

—Hit any of 'em, he said at last, his voice a gargle-murmur.

—And here, is that C sharp or C natural?

—Yeah, one a them.

He kept all his music very close to him, didn't like other people seeing it, he kept everything close to him. When he went out he

Cause, of course, if you're not carefully anchored, a sound can carry you with it. Then where are you? Truth is, you don't know. How many times have you heard a song and been transported into a scene. A place. Not the memory of a place, man, it's a volume you've entered. Internal pressure: it's why you can open your mouth under water. Go too deep, man, too fast... it's impossible to drown a thing crushed under pressure. It feels, smells, there are tastes. Salt. There's sweat. Heavy? But, that's the easy one... often you can make up a memory to put yourself at the scene. A deep listener's alibi. Those aren't memories, they're stage directions. They're narration. Fur coat laid down over a puddle. Puddle with no bottom.

liked to be wrapped up in a coat - winter was his time - and he preferred not to stray too far. At the studio he'd have his music in a little book, reluctant to let other people see it, always plunging it back into his coat pocket when he was through, locking it away.

During the day he walked around, wrapped up in himself, figuring out his music, watching TV or composing when he felt like it. Sometimes he paced for four or five days in a row, walking the streets at first, going south as far as 60th, north as far as 70th, west as far as the river and three blocks east, then gradually restricting his orbit until he was walking around the block and then sticking to the rooms of the apartment, pacing nonstop, hugging the walls, never touching the piano, never sitting - then sleeping for two days straight through.

There were also days when he was stranded between things; when the grammar of moving through the day, the syntax holding events together fell apart. Lost between words, between actions, not knowing something as simple as getting through a door, the rooms of the apartment becoming a maze. The use of things eluded him; the association between an object and its function was not automatic. Entering a room, he seemed surprised that this is what a door existed for. He ate food as if he was astonished by it, as if a roll or sandwich was infinitely mysterious, like he had no recollection of the taste from last time. Once he sat through dinner, peeled an orange like he'd never seen one before, silent all the while until, looking down at the long curl of peel, he said:

—Shapes, a huge grin breaking over his face.

Other times, when he felt the world encroaching, he became very still, retreated right down inside himself. He'd sit still, so calm he looked asleep even with his eyes open, breath moving the hairs of his beard slightly. There is footage of him sitting so still that only the drifting smoke tells you it's not a photograph. Talking to Monk anyway was like talking transatlantic, a delay in things getting through - not a split second but ten seconds sometimes, so long you had to ask a question three or four times over. If he got tense the delays in responding to stimuli of any kind got longer and longer until there was no response at all, his eyes coating over like ice on a pond. Most of the times he

got into difficulties were when he was apart from Nellie or in unfamiliar surroundings. If something went wrong and he felt threatened he'd disconnect very suddenly, shut himself off like a light.

If Nellie was around when he got lost in himself like that she made sure everything was OK and waited for him to find his way out. Even then she felt good being with him as he went maybe four or five days without saying a word until he broke his speech-fast and called out:

—Nellie! Ice cream!

—Whatever it was inside him was very delicate, he had to keep it very still, slow himself right down so that nothing affected it. Even his pacing was a way of retaining his stillness, like a waiter on a ship at sea juggling a glass of water through all sorts of angles just to keep it upright. He'd keep pacing until what was inside him became so tired of twitching around that he could collapse exhausted. These are only guesses, it was impossible to know what was going on in his head. He looked through his glasses sometimes like an animal that's been hibernating, checking to see if it is warm enough to emerge again. He was surrounded by his home, by his eccentricities, then by his silence. One time when we'd been sitting together a couple of hours and he hadn't said anything I asked him:

—What's it like in that head of yours, Monk?

Took his glasses off, held them up to his eyes, and turned them around as if they framed the face of an optician peering into his eyes.

—Take a look. I stepped forward, put my head into the glasses, studied his eyes. Sadness, lively flecks of something.

—See anythin?

—Nope.

—Shit. Haha... Reached up and put the glasses back on his head. Lit a cigarette.

I used to ask Nellie similar things. She knew him better than anybody, so well that whatever I asked her, no matter how weird Monk was acting, she'd say,

—Oh, that's just Thelonious.

⑤
And, then, what of the other direction? Where you're taken, undeniably, out. Or up. The brain reels thru what it knows and comes up empty. Again and again. No frame for the place it's put you. High Pressure: open your mouth and there's no worry about what might rush in. Open your mouth any old way up there and everything you have flies out. High enough, it can get absolutely physical.

nude he's on fire he climbs over the rocks on the breakwater and opens the blue with his body

Monk was helpless without her.
She told him what to wear, helped him into his clothes on the days when he seemed too bewildered even to dress himself, when he got straitjacketed in the sleeves of his suit or lost in the intricacies of knotting his tie. Her pride and fulfilment came from making it possible for him to create his music. She was so integral to his creative well-being that she may as well be credited as co-composer for most of his pieces.

She did everything for him: checking in bags at airports, looking after his passport while he stood still as a column or whirled and shambled around, people looking at him, passing around him wondering what he was doing there, shuffling around like a down-and-out, tossing his arms out like he's throwing confetti at a wedding, wearing one of his crazy hats from some part of the world he'd just come back from. And when he was on the plane and Nellie buckled his seat belt over his overcoat, people would still be wondering who he was, the head of some African state lurching toward independence or something. There were times when Nellie looked at him and wanted to cry - not because she pitied him, but because she knew one day he would die and there was no one else like him in the world.

When Nellie was in the hospital he
sat and smoked, watched a dusty sunset peer in through the rain-grimed windows. He glanced up at the clock hanging from the wall at a surrealist tilt. Nellie had this thing about stuff being straight; Monk preferred things crooked and to get her used to the idea he'd nailed the clock to the wall like that. Every time she looked at it it made her laugh.

He walked from room to room, stood in the places she stood, sat in her chair, looked at her lipstick and makeup, her glasses case and other stuff. Before going to the hospital she had tidied everything away. He touched the fabric of her dresses hanging neat and empty in the closet, looked at the shoes waiting for her in rows.

She did so many things for him that most objects in the apartment were a mystery to

him and he saw them for the first time: the casserole dish, stained from years of use, the steam iron. He picked up her pots and pans, missing the familiar noise of their clanking together. He sat at the piano, building a tune out of all the sounds he missed as she moved around the apartment: the rustle of her clothes as she got dressed, water running in the sink, the clatter of plates. She called him Melodious Thunk and he wanted to write a song for her that sounded just like that. Every five minutes he got up and peered out of the window, checking in case she was heading up the street.

Each day when he visited her she was more worried about him than herself. He sat by the side of her bed, not speaking, smiling when the nurses asked if everything was OK. He stayed for the full duration of visiting time because there was nothing else he wanted to do.

Reluctant to return to the apartment, he walked over to the Hudson to watch the sun set over the freeway expanse of water. A famished wind snatched the smoke from his cigarette. He thought about Nellie and the song he was writing for her, a private thing for piano that no one else would touch. Once he'd written it it would be finished - he'd play it just as it was, unaccompanied with no improvising. He didn't want Nellie to change and he didn't want his song about her to change either. As he looked out across the river a smear of yellow-brown light welled up over the skyline like paint squeezed from a tube. For a few minutes the sky was a blaze of dirty yellow until the light faded and oil-spill clouds sagged again over New Jersey. He thought about heading back to the apartment but stayed on in the sad twilight and watched dark boats crawl over the water, the grief of gulls breaking over them.

Driving to a gig at the Comedy
Store, Baltimore. With him, Nica and Charlie Rouse, friends for life. Virtually everything Monk did he did for life. Pulled into a motel in Delaware. Monk was thirsty, which meant he had to have a drink. Everything was like that with him - he'd stay up three or four days

In electrocutions the lungs can come straight up and out of the mouth. Like Donny B, the other Donny, of course, this is back when I was the other Donny, when we were all just kids in Carr Square. "St. Louis Blues." He'd climbed the telephone pole to pronounce a toast to my birthday when that beer can hit the insulator. What then? A flash like red and blue lightning and he's on his back in the street. A half-swallowed octopus. Who are you going to be then? Victor kneeling over him, clearing his mouth for his make-up-your-F-in-summer-school's worth of CPR and wiping his hand on his jeans. Victor pulling Donny B's lungs out of his mouth and wiping them on his jeans. High pressure. That sound echoing down the street. That sound and my wide open mouth. Then you're us, backing up down the wet street, streaks of lung on Victor's jeans, and smoke coming out of that boy's mouth. Height. After that, you can bet, part of you is always backing up down the wet street...

Ok, height. But what if you're playing it?

You've disappeared.

straight because he didn't feel like sleep and then he'd sleep solidly for two days, anywhere. If he wanted something he had to have it. He walked into the lobby, filling the doorframe, looking dark as a shadow to the desk clerk who jumped slightly when he saw him. Unnerved not just by his blackness, his size, but by the way he ambled in there like an astronaut. Something about him, not just the eyes either, his whole bearing, looking like a statue that might fall over at any moment. And something else too: that morning the booking clerk had scouted around his apartment for clean underwear. Unable to find any, he'd put on a pair of shorts he'd already worn for three long days, blemished yellow and giving off a vague smell, he kept wondering if other people noticed. Monk happened to sniff as he came into the room and that did it; that was one of the things that did it. Maybe nothing would have happened if he'd had clean shorts, but as it was, the slight stickiness, the itch that had been there all day became unbearable when this huge coloured walked in, sniffing the air like it was dirty. Immediately he said there were no rooms, before Monk had even uttered a word. Staring, wearing a crazy hat like he was a pope or cardinal in Africa.

—Saywhaman? Whatever he said lost in a saliva-strangle of sound. A voice like it was coming over the radio from Mars.

—No vacancies. I'm afraid we have no rooms.

—Tayuhglassawar.

—Water?

—Yauh.

—You want water?

Monk nodded like a sage, standing in front of the man, like he was getting in his way, obstructing his view. Something about him was making the desk clerk shake with anger. The way he was standing there, like a striker on a picket line, determined not to budge. Couldn't get a fix on him, not a hobo, dressed… dressed - shit, he couldn't tell rightly how he was dressed: tie, suit, coat - the clothes were smart but he looked a mess, like his shirttails were hanging out or like he was not wearing socks.

—No water, the booking clerk said finally, the words gurgling out like the first rusty belch of water from a tap suddenly twisted.

—No water, he said again, clearing his throat. He was more frightened now, the coloured's yellow eyes staring at him like two planets in space. Even more unnerving was the way Monk was staring not at his eyes but at a spot two inches above them. Quickly he passed a hand over his forehead, feeling for a zit.

—No water. You hear me?

The coloured stood there, like he'd turned to stone, like he'd gone into some nigger trance. He'd never seen anyone so black. Now he was thinking that the coloured was maybe mentally defective in some way, dangerous, a maniac. Staring at him like that.

—You hear me, boy - he felt more confident now, as soon as he called him boy he felt the situation becoming less a specific confrontation between two individuals, more something general, like he had people on his side, backing him up, a man with a mob behind him.

—This a hotel you don't got a glassawar? Must be lot a thirsty muthafuckahs all them full rooms you got.

—Don't get smart, don't even think about getting smart…

At that moment Monk moved a step forward, blocking the light completely, becoming a silhouette; looking into his face was like stepping into a cave on a bright day.

—Now we don't want any trouble here, said the booking clerk. The word "trouble" smashed like a bottle. His chair squeaked back an involuntary inch, anxious to keep the same distance between him and this man looming over him like a cliff. The clerk looked down at the coloured's hands hanging at his side, a big cheek-ripping ring on one finger. That's when it occurred to him that if he had a gun he'd have pulled it on him - looking back on it later he realized it was this thought on his part rather than anything the coloured had done that escalated the situation. Each word

No amount of clapping and shouting can bring you back. Ever. No lie smart enough to conjure your flesh back inside the skin. Can't be done anymore than we could have stuffed Victor's jeans back down D's smoking chest. Bone back into bone. Pressure. It's already happened. So, turn the volume down.

It's a little mystic, isn't it?

Man, one with the spirit? Not hardly. It's gothic. A medieval cathedral lit by torches. Those soaring stones, high arches. Ever hear music in one of those? Think of it back then without modern lights. Smell it. Remember, for heat, most people slept with their sheep and goats in the towering shadow. There's the sound. The height. Inside. The gothic arch, they brought height inside. The ceiling obscured by shadow and smoke. And the songs, polyphony shoots along the stones and up out of sight. Cause that's just about it, isn't it? Maybe it's more like the volume of sights than sounds? People go blind from pressure in their eyes.

triggered the next. The word "trouble" pulled the word "gun" out of its holster and the word "gun" brought the word "police" hurrying after it.

—Like I said, we don't want no trouble here, so you leave quickly or I'm calling the police.

Standing there, dumb as stone, dumb like the only two words he knew were "glass" and "water." The expression on his face had changed now, like he wasn't seeing anything at all, like he didn't know where he was, no idea. Swelling up in himself like he might explode at any moment. The clerk was almost too terrified to dial the police, worried that might be the action to spring him out of whatever he was in - but doing nothing was even more frightening. Decided the way to do it was as blatantly as possible, tugging the phone over, picking the receiver up slowly, dialling like he was dipping his finger in a pot of maple syrup.

—Police? All the time he was speaking he kept one eye, both eyes, on the coloured, whose only movement was the rise and fall of his chest. Breath.

—Well, he's refusing to leave. Standing there like I don't know, like he's gonna cause trouble… I've told him that… Yes, I think he might be dangerous.

He had just replaced the phone - slowly, like everything he was doing now - when another coloured and some rich-looking woman came bustling into the lobby.

—Thelonious? What's happened? Before he had a chance to speak the booking clerk intervened.

—This freak with you? His fear was subsiding, he felt confident now of his ability to goad the situation any which way he liked. The woman looked at him like he was an insect crawling along a wall. The kind of woman who wherever she went would be surrounded by lawns of privilege; even her politeness a form of contempt, the friendliness she lavished on some serving to remind others of the riches they were excluded from.

—What's going on, Thelonious? Still not speaking, just that glare turned on the booking clerk.

—You'd better stick around, lady. The police are on their way and they'll want to ask some questions.

—What?

—Be here any minute.

By some tacit agreement the woman - sounding like the queen of England - and the other coloured manoeuvred him out of the lobby, back to the car. Monk had got into the driver's seat and turned the engine on just as the cops arrived, three of them clambering out of the car. The desk clerk ushered them over to the automobile, keeping in back, out of sight. A flurry of questions, the cops barely polite, not knowing what to make of it but knowing some show of nightstick authority was called for. Told him to turn off the key, the engine. He ignored them, stared straight ahead like he was concentrating hard on the road on a foggy night, unsure of the way. One of the cops reached in, twisted off the ignition himself. The English woman saying something.

—Lady, you just keep quiet. I want everybody outta the car. Him first… Hey, you, get outta the car.

The coloured hunched over the wheel, hands perfectly positioned like he was the captain on the bridge of a ship passing through a storm.

—Listen, you fuckin deaf or somethin? Outta the car, get outta the fuckin car.

—Let me handle this, Steve.

Pushing his head close to Monk's face, the second cop spoke quietly, hissing practically.

—Hey, you dumb-ass nigger, you got about ten seconds to get outta this fuckin car before I pull you out. You hear that?

The coloured sitting there, big shoulders, still wearing the crazy pope hat.

—OK, you have it your way. Instantly grabbed him by the shoulders, pulling him half out of the car, but his hands were still clinging to the steering wheel like he was handcuffed to it.

—Goddam. The cop started pulling at his wrists, which were thick, corded with muscle, immovable. The English bitch yelling, the cops yelling too.

Sphere's aren't always enough. You know? The world as we find it? Not enough, sometimes we need better than optimal. Three dimensions worth of perfect won't get it. Volume over space. Any ratio greater than one: depth. Less than one: height. Stay too far from one, for too long and it's lights out, either way. Heraclitus sings Blues for Pythagorus.

The pressure of heights. It won't come in from out there. Forget out there. If your high, it's already inside and if it's inside it's on the loose, searching for a way out. Depth, the constant sensation of being surrounded. Suspended in sound. Depth: fear of invasion. Height: of spontaneous effusion.

—Lemme get at this dumb-fuck . . . Getting in each other's way, one of them drawing his nightstick and pounding it down on Monk's hands, hard and fast as he could in the confines of the car, hard enough to draw blood, making the knuckles puff up and the English woman screaming about he's a pianist, his hands, his hands . . .

At the Vanguard it was packed, Monk playing solo. A couple of college students bartered with the doorman, trying to get a table right up close by the piano.

—You kidding? You get here halfway through the set and expect a table at the front. People want to see his hands, man…

At a hotel in Boston he walked around the lobby for an hour and a half, inspecting the walls, peering at them like they were pictures, running his hands over them, orbiting the room, alarming guests. Asked for a room and was told to get out before there was any trouble. Leaving the hotel, he walked the revolving doors for ten minutes, pushing patiently like a pit pony. At that night's gig he played two numbers and left the stage. An hour later he came back, played the same two songs again and then sat staring at the piano for half an hour until the band left the stage and the manager played "Who Knows" over the PA. People got up to leave, wondering if they'd seen him crack up before their eyes. No one jeered or complained, a couple of people spoke to him, touched his shoulder, but he made no response. It was as if everyone had stepped thirty years into the future into an installation entitled "Thelonious Monk at the Piano," a museum exhibit simulating the atmosphere of jazz clubs of old.

Later, in a panic dash to find Nellie and head for the airport, he was stopped by a state trooper. Frazzled by tiredness, he refused to say a word, not even his name. He slept for a long time, dreamed he was in the hospital and when he woke he found he was eating food spooned to him in bed, looking up at nurses like a man trapped beneath the rubble of a collapsed building. Lights peered into his eyes like he was an animal. Held himself close, in possession of a secret so precious he had forgotten what it was. People had been saying he was crazy for so long that he shuffled along in Lowell pyjamas like someone who had been there a long time. Played a few chords on the piano and the doctors thought they noticed some untutored musical instinct twitching from his hands, hitting notes that had a kind of ugly beauty. Tinkly, thunking things. Other patients liked his playing, one howling along, another joining in with a song about a man and a faithful horse that died, a couple of others just crying or laughing.

Silence settled on him like dust. He went deep inside himself and never came out.

—What do you think the purpose of life is?

—To die.

He spent the last ten years of his life at Nica's place just across the river in New Jersey, a view of Manhattan filling the tall windows, lived there with Nellie and the kids too. He didn't touch the piano because he didn't feel like it. Saw no one, rarely talked or got out of bed, enjoyed simple sensations like smelling a bowl of flowers, seeing the leaves spongy with dust.

—I'm not sure what happened to him. It was like he was in the grip of a prolonged flinch - like something had grazed him, as if he had stepped out into traffic and a car had just missed him. He got lost inside the labyrinth of himself and puttered around there, never found a way out.

Maybe nothing happened to him externally. Only the weather in his own head was important and suddenly everything clouded over as it had many times before - but this time for ten years. It wasn't despair, almost the opposite: a form of contentment so extreme that it was almost torpor, like when you stay in bed for a whole day, not because you can't bear to face the horror of the day, but because you don't feel like it, because it's nice lying there. Everyone has that impulse to do nothing but it rarely takes root. Monk was used to always doing what he felt like and if he

---

Seems easy to talk about it. But, you're never really talking about it. Webs of refraction and inversion. Takes a *song*, a sound that can do more than one thing at a time. It's the danger of singing. That's what a song is. Got to where, if I even got close to a piano. I remember when I was little, every piano I saw sounded to me like broken voices. I couldn't play, really, but I could sit down and I'd just know how to fix the voices. I got good at fixing voices, until, I began to hear things behind the voices. Later, man, if I was anywhere near a piano, got to where it felt just like sitting next to a roaring river. Spring run off. That weight and speed and thunder. Problem was it felt like I couldn't really find it. I could hear it, but, couldn't find where it'd come from. And it seemed then that I'd have to swim the roar before I could hear. Let alone fix, the voices again. There are the keys, but, I'm lost in the sound. Like I can hear it in the distance and at the same time it's running right thru me but I can't find it. Soaking wet, dying of thirst. Lost in and locked out of it? High, a song lost in the distance. Or, or. Ice. Like I'd slipped, lost traction. To where I could feel myself skating. Like I was dying of weightlessness, could feel gravity, a pull. But, into what?

   Afraid of the falls?

I was afraid, man. Damn straight. But, not of falling. Or Swimming or drowning. Not even of being lost.

felt like staying in bed for ten years he'd do that, regretting nothing, wanting nothing. He was at the mercy of himself. He had no self-discipline because he'd never needed any. He'd worked when he felt like it and now he no longer felt like it. He no longer felt like anything.

–Yes, I would say there was a lot of sadness in him. The things that happened to him, most of it stayed in him. He let a little of that out in music, not as anger, just a bit of sadness here and there. "Round Midnight," that's a sad song.

Autumn in New York, a brown sludge of leaves underfoot, a light rain barely falling. Halos of mist around trees, a clock waiting to strike twelve. Almost your birthday, Monk.

The city quiet as a beach, the noise of traffic like a tide. Neon sleeping in puddles. Places shutting and staying open. People saying goodbye outside bars, walking home alone. Work still going on, the city repairing itself.

At some time all cities have this feel: in London it's at five or six on a winter evening. Paris has it too, late, when the cafes are closing up. In New York it can happen anytime: early in the morning as the light climbs over the canyon streets and the avenues stretch so far into the distance that it seems the whole world is city; or now, as the chimes of midnight hang in the rain and all the city's longings acquire the clarity and certainty of sudden understanding. The day coming to an end and people unable to evade any longer the nagging sense of futility that has been growing stronger through the day, knowing that they will feel better when they wake up and it is daylight again but knowing also that each day leads to this sense of quiet isolation. Whether the plates have been stacked neatly away or the sink is cluttered with unwashed dishes makes no difference because all these details - the clothes hanging in the closet, the sheets on the bed - tell the same story - a story in which they walk to the window and look out at the rain-lit streets, wondering how many other people are looking out like this: people who look forward to Monday because the weekdays have a purpose which vanishes at the weekend when there is only the laundry and the papers. And knowing also that these thoughts do not represent any kind of revelation because by now they have themselves become part of the same routine of bearable despair, a summing up that is all the time dissolving into the everyday. A time of the day when it is possible to regret everything and nothing in the same breath, when the only wish of all bachelors is that there was someone who loved them, who was thinking of them even if she was on the other side of the world. When a woman, feeling the city falling damp around her, hearing music from a radio somewhere, looks up and imagines the lives being led behind the yellow-lighted windows: a man at his sink, a family crowded together around a television, lovers drawing curtains, someone at his desk, hearing the same tune on the radio, writing these words.

Geoff Dyer writes. Most recently, *The Ongoing Moment*. This piece is culled his book about jazz, *But Beautiful*.

None of the metaphors scared me. It was that none of the songs I knew interested me. It was the crushing sense of all of it happening at once. Everywhere. To everyone. And the sense of people so obviously steeled against noticing. Afraid of what might happen. And the kicker: it's already happened. August 18, 1950, in his diary, this is toward the end, shit this *is* the end: Pavese wrote: 'The thing most feared in secret always happens.' I don't think so. No, has *already* happened. He thought it was a fear of depths. But it wasn't depth, the fear, it was heights. That's the fear. It's in there already. That's the height. No. If it hadn't already happened, the romantics would be enough. They'd be perfect but for the *height*. But, for what's already happened, what's already in there–

The grass in Queenstown was pink in 1996. Or, at least, so it seemed to Antjie Krog, one bright winter morning after days of dark skies. A feeble footed sun tried in vain to pierce obstinate clouds shrouding the small Eastern Cape town. Queenstown was dark during most of the time the TRC held its human rights violations hearings there. It was dark and the sky was weeping. It was a week of weeping, as victim after victim narrated to the country and the world their pain. I was also damn depressed and ill during my stay there. I caught a bad cold - more fuel for a particular curiosity I had been nursing for over a decade about the psyche of that town.

It all began in the year of fire this curiosity, for me, this fascination, really, with the frontier town. '85 was the year of fire in South Africa's modern history of turbulence. In that year die Groot Krokodil declared the first state of emergency in a few magisterial districts. The declaration listed some of the predictable trouble spots, like Duduza and the Vaal triangle. But Queenstown too was included, which at the time seemed odd. Why Queenstown? I remember wondering. I also remember that the popular press and broadcast services were of no help in answering the question.

Duduza, the Vaal triangle and even Cradock were obvious targets of the first emergency regulations because they were literally on fire. In Duduza, Maki Skhosana was one of the first victims of a series of necklace murders that spread through the country like a veld fire in that year and onwards. Her's was also a much publicised case. The SABC screened some seriously gruesome footage on the girl's murder at a funeral in the township. In absolute disgust, Bishop Tutu threatened to leave the country - "If the violence continues, I will pack my bags, collect my family and leave this beautiful country that I love so passionately and so deeply," he said. Duduza was burning.

The Vaal triangle, at the same time, claimed its spot in the year's violent calendar of uprising with what became known, later, as the Sharpeville 6 trial. Before the Sharpeville 6, the township was known for the massacre that had taken place there in the 60s when protesters against the pass laws were shot

and killed. It came as little surprise that PWB had included the place in his state of emergency.

Cradock, as small as it is, was also a predictable inclusion because of its high media profile during the Matthew Goniwe crisis at Lingelethu Secondary School. Before the Goniwe crisis and his subsequent assassination, Cradock, to those who know it, was not really the small innocent Karoo town that people make it out to have been. In fact between Cradock, Graaf-Reinet and Beaufort West there was an ongoing competition for the number one spot in stone throwing in the Karoo. Beaufort West later won the title in the late 80s, when they brought down a police helicopter with a rock. Pundits in the stone-throwing department are still at loggerheads about where the title resided before the Beaufort West incident. There are some who say it was in Graaf Reinet, where Chief Mangosuthu Buthelezi was stoned at the funeral of Robert Sobukwe in 1978. Others disagree, saying that while the geography was Graaf Reinet, the actual stone throwers were mostly from Cradock. The real answer lies somewhere between struggle mythology and urban legend and, whatever it is, it does not answer the Queenstown issue - the matter of that frontier town's mystique.

The town's oddity first drew my attention when my roommate at the Wits students' residence in Mofolo, Soweto, exclaimed at the number of necklace murders in Queenstown. Whatever his source was, it declared Queenstown the country's unofficial necklacing headquarters. Queenstown in 1985 had more necklace murders than Duduza or any other place in unrest stricken South Africa. The question, for me, was "Why?"

The more questions I asked, the deeper the mystery of Queenstown became. I discovered from a friend who lives there that the town housed two mental hospitals for a greater part of the 70s and 80s. The reason for this apparently had to do with the division of Queenstown into two parts when the Transkei was declared a homeland in 1976. One part, which continued to be called Queenstown, remained South African; the other, under the name Queensdale, became a part of the Transkei. With this division, the inmates

So, you see, it's not that people don't like good music. It's that they're afraid of heights. Ears pop. Mouths clenched. Look around you, see if people aren't holding themselves tight, like they're afraid of what they might do. Like they're standing on a cliff. That draw from over the edge… Like they're afraid to move. Look. Afraid of what might fly out under pressure… Their mouths don't even look like mouths, really, afraid of what they might say. Mouths look more like padlocks than mouths. Eyes behind the bars. And Depth. Others won't stop moving, couldn't stand still for a minute. Like a building that has to sway to stand. Depth, been down too long for down to bother me – Next verse should say 'someone stop me before I say the next thing and scare the life out of myself…someone teach me how to stop. & how to fall.' Depth. Want to know why you feel surrounded? Because you're surrounded.

You ain't gonna know ME
Cos U think U know ME
— Mongs

of the mental hospital had to be separated into two categories: the Queenstown and the Queensdale patients. A new mental hospital was built for Queensdale, just across the road from the old Queenstown facility. When I heard of this (circa 1989), I came to the only possible conclusion: the whole place was off its mind. By the time I heard the reason behind the two hospitals in 1996 I was certain Queenstown was a loony bin.

Then I learned something else about the town - a curious aspect of musical history. A few years ago, from someone living around there, I discovered that some of the biggest names in South African music were born in or lived in Queenstown - some say what is now known as South African Jazz was invented in the town. Amongst them: Victor Ndlazolwana; the Matshikiza dynasty, which includes the famous pianist Pat, who composed many of choral gems that are classics in their genre, and his younger brother Todd, who wrote the score for *King Kong* the musical; Dudu Pukwana, who made a name for himself in London and Europe; Mongezi Feza, who composed a song that adds to the mystique of his birth place: *You Ain't Gonna Know Me ('Cos You Think You Know Me)*; Letta Mbulu, who came to fame in the States in collaboration with husband Caiphus Semenya and Quincy Jones; Margaret Singana, who was actually Mcingana, and is also known as Lady Africa; Don Tshomela, by far the most famous jazz singer alive in the country at the moment; Stompie Mavi, the man with a golden voice who is currently having a beautiful revival with Joe Nina.

Many of these artists are late. Dudu Pukwana died in London. Todd Matshikiza died in exile. Mongezi Feza ran naked out of a mental hospital in Switzerland and froze to death. Margaret Mcingana was confined to a wheel chair before she died last year. Johnny Dyani expired on stage while playing bass in Berlin.

At the time of the discovery of the Queenstown music epic, I was flattened by a strange coincidence that was just too odd to ignore. Both Stompie Mavi and Margaret Mcingana were in wheelchairs. "Queenstown is a place of black magic," my informant pointed out. "The musicians there are all special people. It is a special madness."

Indeed, in Xhosa culture, the singer or musician is supposed to have *inkenqe* or *intwaso* - a particular spirituality usually possessed by sangoma. Schizophrenia in the Xhosa tradition is not recognised as a disease. It is a special attribute one possesses. Many schizophrenics undergo a process called *ukuthwasa* and end up sangomas. Much of this process involves music. Ezra Ngcukana, a jazz saxophonist in Cape Town, recommending that I speak to Stompie Mavi, says, "Stompie and Don Tshomela sing like they have been granted special permission by the ancestry." He also reminds me of a nickname Queenstown has, that I knew about but had granted little importance before then: *emagezeni* - "place of the mad people."

Queenstown, then, is known as a place of madness both for its mental hospitals and its musicians. "You will get ill if you go to Queenstown," Tshomela says to me. I tell him that, yes, I did fall ill there in 1996, during the TRC hearings, and he asks, "Are you an artist?" I tell him that I am a poet. "Well there you go!" he says. "Strange coincidence," Bra Don continues, "I am leaving for Queenstown day after tomorrow. Why don't you come and see me?"

Cape Town, April 2002

→ *Bra Don died in CT, 2004*

Sandile Dikeni is the author of two collections of poems *Guava Juice* and *Telegraph to the Sky*, and a collection of essays, *Soul Fire*. He lives in Cape Town.

Chimu peep

Like I say, on some level, people must know this stuff. In the ward, I used to see a man who'd walk the halls all day long. Strangest gait you've ever seen. A shuffle. Right foot in back, left out front. Picture him: right perpendicular to the line of motion, left in the line of motion. He'd lean on his back, right, foot and gradually shift his weight to his left in front. As he shifted his weight he'd gradually move the back foot up to the front. Upside down capital T position. Then, shifting back to the metal, he'd slide the left foot forward. Strangest thing. Repeated, absolutely without variation that I could see. Miles like that. Deliberate. All day. Serious. All the while there was any forward motion, always with the same foot, all his weight was anchored to the back foot, straddling the path. And, all at once I saw it. Of course, it's how you inch up to a cliff. The pull of the cliff. He didn't fear heights. Forget duality and the broken dialectics of strip-tease and musical chairs. He wasn't saying shit. He knew it, everyone else knew it. Hard-core monist: he was afraid of this one thing, this only thing : this everything : this falling. And his face matter-of-fact: "I know I'm not getting far, but, I'm not falling for it." I thought, that's us, all of us, even pedal to the metal, passing uphill around a curve at night. That's still us. The illusion of motion. Speed's the most popular kind of noise we know. It's why the more time you think you've saved the less time you feel like you have. Volume is a ruse for the bone-deaf. The way speed is a lie told by the stuck-in-the-mud.

Words by Ed Pavlic, from

Open on the table in the sunlight, I glimpsed his file one day, written in the doctor's hand on the pad... "Patient exhibits great care to avoid, what he terms, a 'potentially catastrophic loss of altitude.'" I know my mouth was wide open. And I could hear this wild laughter coming from across the common room.

on fire   *over the rocks on the breakwater with his body*

forthcoming: "Winners have yet to be announced" — a song for Donny Hathaway

Matthew
Goniwe as
seen by
Julian Cobbing
in Joza (1985)
2 mnths before
he was
assassinated

(with
Sparrow
Mkhonto,
Sicelo Mhlanli)
Fort Catala)

(THE PICTURE)

The picture
swayed from side
to side like a feather,
and then landed face up. Black and
white. A boy. No older than 16. The expression
in the eyes, the anger, so concentrated. The
deep contrast of the grainy image accentuates
the boy's contorted body as he flings a
petrol bomb, its flame a white streak. His
arm creates a blur as it swings the flaming
cocktail. His eyes are focused intensely at
something outside the picture. There have
been many moments in South Africa when one
could have taken that picture. Anonymous,
angry, black. Timeless. That's what I would
tell you if I didn't know you.

But that picture is not anonymous.
I took it in August 1985, on Belgravia Road
in Athlone. Near where Ali's corner shop used
to be. We had just come from Gugs and some
of the other nearby townships. The police
were breaking up a meeting kids were having
at a school. It was hectic ek sê. All hell
broke loose when the police shot teargas into
the hall. Students hysterically running off
in different directions. Police with batons.
Shotguns. We got some good images of them
shooting at the kids - while the kids were
running away. I was with Associated at the
time and knew I had a wire service deadline,
so I decided to head back to town. The army
had also decided to try and clear the area of
journalists, like they would often do before

insert red

insert green

insert white

hey mr. writer, why don't you tell it like it really is?

the State of Emergency. So they could run amok in the townships - "mopping up operations" they used to call it, I think.

I had a kid with me. From Minnesota. Pete, Peter Jackson. Freelancing. I was reluctant - not in the mood to be the guide for a trophy hunter - but he begged me that morning to let him tag along. There were loads of them at that time. Some of the big names. Some trying to make it. And this was a chance to make it. If you were prepared to go where more established types, or those who had families and so on, would not go, then you would sell a pic or two. Make a name for yourself. It's still like that today of course, Gaza, Kabul, Freetown. He seemed alright. He was trying to make it like we all were at some stage. Somebody hooked him up with me - I had a car. We could still get cars then from the rental agencies. Later on they stopped giving us cars altogether. Couldn't afford having so many cars wrecked every day. Stones through windscreens, bullet holes, burnt out. The insurance companies are not actually in the habit of underwriting disasters, no matter what they might say in the ads. I let Peter hitch a ride.

I knew the area, the townships, the Cape Flats. It's where I grew up. Things were very competitive. Access depended on your contacts on the street. People would page me, page others, saying shit's going down, or the cops are shooting here, detaining someone there, and we would rush over, get the pic, get out, put it on the wire. There was competition. Who could get the picture out first was a big thing. If your agency had it first, they could sell it first. Bottom line.

I didn't really like the internationals. I didn't like a lot of the locals either. There was tension between us. There were different groups. Different ways of doing things. Lots of problems. But we got along. Most of the time.

Well, you know, this kid, hanging out with me, he could get to places the other internationals couldn't. By that time I was also passing pics to the anti-apartheid movement, gratis, pasella, and my agency didn't know. As long as there was no by-line I could get away with it. But when they found out, that was to be one of the things that put an end to our relationship. Anyway, because of this I knew

some of the underground people too, so they would also keep me informed.

That day, as we were heading back to the city centre so we could send our stuff out, I got paged that there was something happening in Athlone, in Belgravia Road. We were driving by on the way to town, so I said let's go.

When we got there, things seemed quite still. The shops were trading normally, traffic flowing smoothly. No mothers and aunties out on the stoeps. I hadn't even noticed that somewhere along the line normality was something that I had learnt to be suspicious of. I stopped the car at Ali's shop, told Peter to stay in the car. Said my salaams and chatted to Ali for a while. Bought some smokes. He said the students were having a meeting. We drove past the school to peek in. It looked quite reserved. To kill time we popped in to see some kids staying at a place nearby in Osterly Road. Had some coffee. Caught up on the latest developments at the University of the Western Cape. From their lounge, I could catch a glimpse of the school. A police casspir went by. Slowly. I could see another one in the far distance. The green and brown camouflage standing out rudely, in this very average residential area. This was a camouflage that was meant almost *not* to camouflage. Suppose that's why the police later used vans that were an almost luminous lemon, just to make them even more noticeable. The kids would call them mello-yellos. They're the same ones they use now, nogal. Between you and me, I still get a bit of a skrik when I see a yellow casspir in my rear-view mirror.

I could hear the sound of students singing and the rumble of toyi-toying. "Zenzenina, Zenzenina, what have we done, what have we done." They were planning to march with their placards to Athlone police station, which was nearest. That was the plan. They wouldn't get out of the school gates. I ran back to the car. Peter was restlessly lighting up a cigarette. We drove around the school and parked close by. I could see more police vehicles, some unmarked, circling. They noticed us. I knew some of them by now. They knew us. Some kids had come from the townships to Athlone - a thing that never really happened when I was growing up. Divide and rule had worked better then. Now it seemed they were stripping away the differences. When they were being whipped, it didn't matter that they were classified as Coloured or African or Indian. It was equal opportunity oppression. Yet their hope was infectious. Their enthusiasm. The possibilities they showed us. But also tragic. Or maybe old age just beats that enthusiasm out of you? That battering of time against your soul, till you're just floating with the breeze. That's many of us, many of our parents. But these kids. To see them stand up, resilient like taut blades of grass upright against the Cape's south-easterly wind. That was quite a feeling. You have that, don't you? I hope you keep it, hold on to it as long as you can. Savour it. Nurture it my friend.

I recognised one of the kids from Langa. Themba Mtumkulu. That was his name. He ran up to me, shook my hand. "Bra Faze, howzit?" That's what he called me, that's what they called me on the street, Bra Faze.

"It's alright broer," I said, "and you, what's going on? Mass meeting?"
  "Sipho was detained yesterday, did you hear?"
"No!" I exclaimed, surprised and not surprised. "This for him?"
  "Yah, we need to get more support, mobilise the community."
  Then in a spin, he ran off, saying, "Take care, hope you get some good shots," and me shouting back, "Cover your faces." Some tied their handkerchiefs around their faces. Others had taken to wearing the checked scarves that Palestinian kids wear to hide their faces. It hid their identity and gave them one. Soon Themba melted into the big heaving smudge of discontent.

The camera was a double-edged sword. Like seasoned politicians, these kids had learnt that they needed us to get their message out. But it was a fragile affair because they could be identified by the pictures we took. Many had been; and many photographers had been irresponsible about this, shooting pics of kids who would then be put away because of the images they had taken. Those who parachuted in and out with big names and big bucks, they didn't give a shit. Well, most of them anyway. It was also racial. I think the black photographers - the few of us - we were more sensitive to things like security, like protecting people, than most of the other photographers. Probably because these could easily have been, and sometimes were our kids out there on the streets. I remember sitting

with Don McDougal, who won the Pulitzer, in a bar on Long street, and having a moerse argument diep into the darkness of early morning about this. He just didn't give a damn. And it hurt. To have your heroes turn out so ugly, right in front of you. And it wasn't just the whisky. It was as if under the haven of darkness he felt safe enough to reveal the vampire he was.

Well, it didn't take long for the police to act. The usual. Teargas. Then shotguns. Pete and I ran to the back of the school. Jumped the fence, ran through the rows of school blocks till we were amongst the students. I ran for the edges to get a good point of view. It didn't help to be between the kids and the cops. No man's land. "You could get shots, but no pictures," was a corny joke that went around. A writer would say, "There was chaos." But to me there wasn't. In those moments all that noise seems to come together like a finely arranged orchestra. Every move, every gunshot, on cue as if conducted. First movement: cops attack. Second movement: students retreat and regroup. Third movement: students defend. Fourth movement: cops attack, and so it would go on. Adagios. Then rapid staccatoed notes. You tend not to hear a lot of the screaming. You try not to fall over pimply boys and girl-women tripping over each other. Shoes strewn around. You learn to breathe swimming in clouds of teargas, the adrenaline converting the choking gas into crisp Ceres mountain air. You learn to see through the white haze, to focus, to think about composition, to think about film speed, lenses, lighting, deadlines.

The kids responded with a barrage of stones that barely reached the perimeter of police vehicles that lined the school like a thick hedge of yellow and blue thorns. More teargas. A few kids, prepared with their aunties' padded gardening gloves, faces covered with scarves, picked up the ice-hot canister and flung it back at the cops. If it reached its target there would be roars of applause, like appreciation for a well bowled ball in a cricket match. Kids can pick on your weakness like adults cannot. And the faults of the varke, clumsy-fat-sweaty-pink policemen, or manoeuvres that would backfire - like when the wind would blow the teargas back at the cops - would earn well deserved giggles and teasing.

لا لنشر سلاحنا الوسخ

Another kid went for the next round of teargas canisters. I focused on him. He threw. I got the pic. Gunshot. The kid slumped to the ground. A scarlet line ripped across his grey flannel school pants and white shirt. Slapped on a long zoom. Shooting. Shocked. Keep shooting. The motordrive on the camera chowing film faster than you can say sorry, siestog or ag shame. Looked around and saw Pete. Shouting to himself in his midwest accent from behind the camera, "Motherfuckers, motherfuckers," over and over.

Eventually some kids ran over and dragged the shot kid into one of the classrooms. Pete and I crept up behind a low brick wall. I looked over and saw Themba hunched and striding towards the cops. Behind his back, in his hands, a flaming petrol - guava juice. I knew he was going to throw it. I focused. He swung the petrol bomb towards one of the vehicles. It landed with a crackling thud, then the gentle tingling of the shattering glass, and the hour long freeze-frame second before you hear the muted swoosh of flames gasping in all directions. "Get out of here!" I instinctively yelled out to him. Why didn't he cover his face? Why did I take the picture? I realised as soon as I took the camera away from my eye. A policeman, his blue uniform in a red-yellow halo, rolled around frantically as his colleagues wrestled the flames.

In the corner of my eye I saw another cop pointing his finger at us. I shouted at Pete to get out of there, to hide. I knew they would try to take our film. I knew I had shot the image of Themba. If they got my film I knew he was in shit. I ran through the school buildings. My cameras suddenly feeling like concrete slabs to and fro-ing, the straps like cables strangling me. Up the stairs, sweating, slipping, banging the cameras against walls - I could hear them behind me. Ran into a classroom. Lying on the floor. If they looked through the window they would see me. Hear the heavy boots. Stomping. Angry voices. Slamming open doors down the corridor. They were coming closer. I couldn't get out of the classroom. Shit. How I could I be so stupid. I rewound the film. Tried to slip the roll of film out, but the camera-back jammed where I had knocked it. The voices were getting closer. The sound of a dog barking. I pulled hard. It opened. Slipped in another roll. Hoped for the best. The door burst open and a stubby cop I recognised barged in, his red face sweating

profusely as he heaved his body about in his undersized uniform. Oversized shotgun at the ready. "Where is it? Give me your fucking camera!" "No," I said, quoting press freedom rights and all that stuff. "Don't give me that kak, I'll klap your fucking head in right here. Give me the fucking camera," he shouted. I handed him the camera. He grinned, "Thank you very much. That fucking little darkie is going to roast for this!"

I lay there. It felt like hours. Looking up at the ceiling of the classroom. It'd been a long time since I'd been in a classroom. This time I actually feel relieved. I still had the roll of film with the pic on. I am a school-kid again and got away with something naughty. Then I remembered my deadline. Rushed back to the car. Pete was nowhere to be found. Figured that he'd made his way back to town. Send off my film. Then go to Don Pedro's for a shot or two of Johnny Walker. I knew I couldn't go home that night. They would soon find out that I had given them a blank roll of film. They would come looking for me. Luckily I didn't keep any other stuff at home. You had to be careful about things like that. We never stored all our pics or negs in one place. Always moved them around. It was your canvasses, your weapons, all you had. Without them there was nothing to verify what you'd done when you had to account. Where you stood.

I called my wife. The phone just rang but no answer. She was usually home at this time. Or maybe I just really wanted her to be at home. I left a cryptic message on the answering machine. Had another drink. Some of the other journos started pulling in to swap stories about the day's escapades mostly. I wasn't really into that. I didn't like those post-mortems, about close calls, almosts, ifs, buts. Still, I didn't know where else to go. Tried phoning Yasmin again. No answer. Then I remembered she was working nightshift. I would wait it out. Just after midnight a photographer I knew from the Cape Times came into the bar. He had just come off duty and the morning edition was probably at press now.
"Hey, Faze, how you doing? You must've got some great pics you old bastard," he smiled, with a tinge of envy.
"What do you mean?"
"Well, a kid brought in some excellent stuff this afternoon to the picture editor. Said he was with you."

I wasn't sure if Pete had shot a picture of Themba. I put my hand in my pocket just to check if the roll of film was still there. Felt better just knowing it was there. But it didn't help for long. I went over to the Argus building where the papers were printed. A strong South-Easter was kicking the day's junk around. I asked the guys at printing if they had run the paper already. They showed me a copy. Front page pic - Themba throwing the fucking petrol bomb. Fuck! Fuck! How could Pete do this? I had warned him. Told him to be sensitive. I didn't know how to warn Themba. I didn't even know where he stayed. Who his family was. Who his friends were. I knew the townships like the back of my hand. Alley ways and by-ways. Good positions. Friendly taverns and shebeens. Where to buy good zol. But I realised I didn't really know the people.

I went over to Pete's flat. Banged on the door. A young blonde girl opened, angrily demanding to know what my problem was. Eventually Pete came into the lounge, woken up by my loud voice. "What's up," he drawled, surprised. "What the fuck's up? You don't realise what you've done? You've just killed someone you know. I took you there. You were with me. I told you don't shoot the kids if their faces aren't covered. You sold that pic to the *Times* and they're running it, and that kid's gonna get fucked up, that's fucking what!" He looked at me, somewhat dazed. Still a bit stoned; "Come on man, Fazel, don't sweat it. It was a great pic. I had to sell it. Besides, man, there's no way they're gonna pick that kid up, I mean, man, how they gonna find him, recognise him... hell, I wouldn't be able to."

ASSHOLE

All blacks look alike? I didn't bother to let him explain. I just gave a good swing, decked him and walked out. The chick ran after me shouting hysterically.

I still didn't know what to do. I sat in my car outside the building Yasmin worked in. It was a community radio and she handled production, sometimes through the night. The early blue radiance of dawn crept up. I wished I could turn it off. Change the filter. When you make pictures you think you have a lot of power. To decide what to put in the frame, what to leave out. But this time I felt as if I was framed as much as I was doing the framing. I thought I was doing good. But fuck it, now I was part of the problem. The morning light became harsher. The refuge offered by dawn's shadows was now illuminated. Then I saw Yasmin and called out to her. She would go home and if things were alright she would leave an agreed upon message at her mother's place for me. I needed to look for Themba. Drove out of town towards Langa. Avoided the early morning traffic coming in, as people lined up to earn their bread and butter with their normal jobs. Safe jobs. Maybe I should have just done that. Lawyer, accountant or something like that. The jobs that make parents happy. The jobs that make husbands and wives and kids happy. The taxis were darting down Main Road as I passed through Woodstock, then Salt River, then Mowbray. Women of all ages, shapes, sizes, but not races, pouring into the clothing factories where they earned their weekly wage. Streaming in from Bontehuewel, Mannenberg, Mitchells Plain. The morning papers lying in bundles outside the shops, like time bombs waiting to go off. Maybe I could just pick them all up.

I took the turn-off onto the N2 highway. If I just kept going I could head out, away from this whole situation. Cross the Hottentots Holland mountains, like the boere who trekked out of the Cape. But I turn left into Bhunga Avenue, round the sharp bend off the road that delivers you into another world. The townships in Cape Town were designed to be completely unobtrusive. To be polite to the privileged. You could live your whole life in the Coloured and Indian areas on the Cape Flats, in the leafy white suburbs in Claremont, Newlands, or the ocean side areas of Camps Bay and Clifton and not ever go into the townships. Not ever see the joys and sorrows, the life that went on there. Langa was already long awake compared to the sleepy city centre I had just come from. People had to leave early to get to work, by bus, by taxi, by train. They had to prepare the city centre for those who would come in from the suburbs and mess it up, like only ungrateful guests can.

I circled around the school. The place was already bristling with army vehicles skulking around like hyenas, looking to separate the weak from the strong and turn them into breakfast. School kids were making their way through the gates. I asked a few if they knew Themba. Some said they did. Others, suspicious of me, wouldn't talk. Yesterday's tiredness suddenly came up behind me and grabbed me. I made it to my in-laws'. The message from Yasmin said everything was OK at our place.

I slept. The constant buzzing of my beeper eventually woke me at around 2:30pm. The day was almost gone. I flipped through my messages. Three calls from Langa. My heart sank. Anxiously, I called. Cops were there. Early in the morning they came, looking for Themba. They had the picture. I rushed over. The beleaguered principal and some students were milling around. They were angry. I tried to explain. It seemed no use. The wound was still oozing with blood. I felt completely dejected. I hadn't felt this angry at myself, at what I did for a living before. I vaguely realised, on the advice of those who had gone before, that it was a difficult place to make your meaning. But this felt so different. How could I have been so stupid? I should have made sure Pete didn't have the picture. I asked about Themba's parents. Reluctantly, someone gave me an address.

As far as we knew Themba didn't arrive at school that day. I went over to his mother's. She sat distraught in the centre of the tiny lounge. Neighbours shuffled around. The house had been raped and left for dead after the police searched it looking for her son. An old man, recognising me as a journalist, asked me what I wanted. I said I wanted to know where Themba was, if he knew where he was. He showed me the paper. That picture, like a phobia, was paraded in front of me. He didn't say much. All the accusation was there, on the front page. In the furniture strewn across the lounge. On the face of the sobbing mother. I tried to extricate myself, saying that I had not taken it, but neither I nor they seemed convinced of this. I was implicated. The press card I carried was enough.

I did manage to establish that Themba had not come home the previous night. This had not been great cause for alarm as this was not unusual. He was often on the run from the police and rarely slept at home those days. Like butterflies, the young activists bounced from flower to flower, on-the-go all the time. A friend of his told me that Themba had been hiding somewhere, but had left for school. I had just been at the school and we knew he had not arrived. He could be hiding or he could have been picked up. It was hard to say. No one on either side would give up that kind of information readily. I had read in the article that the policeman had been quite badly burnt. Themba would be in for serious trouble if they picked him up. I drove around hoping to catch a glimpse of him.

It was getting late. None of Themba's friends had called back. I decided to go to Caledon Square and ask the police if they had detained him and to demand the camera they had taken from me. I wasn't actually sure that I wanted it back, but it seemed like the right thing to do. As fate would have it, the cop who'd taken my camera was lounging around the information desk. Eventually recognising me, he mused, "Ah, only now? I thought you would have been here ages ago for your stuff. I would have come looking for you," he said, "because you think you're a slimgat, don't you, giving us a roll of blank film. Luckily that boy was all over the papers. We didn't need your picture anyway. Just keep your eyes open my friend. Funny things happen out there." Then he turned his back on me. I asked him if they had arrested the boy. Without turning around he muttered, "Don't you worry about him. He is going to get it good."

I began to panic. This cop seemed too confident. It wouldn't be unlike them to have picked Themba up and not even reported the arrest. Or they could be keeping him somewhere and torturing him. Or worse. My mind convulsed with scenarios and images. I went home.

Over the next few weeks I fell into a deep slump. It was difficult for me to work. Agency demands, bills, bond, debt, all crowding around me. Themba had simply vanished. And no one was talking. The police refused to confirm or deny any knowledge of his whereabouts. All kinds of rumours whispered through Langa about his disappearance. After a few months even his family resigned themselves to speaking of him in the past tense.

I continued to visit Themba's family. In his mother's lounge, a framed class photo of Themba was competing for space in the glass cabinet. The frame was inscribed with the words "Hamba Kahle." He was one of five boys. Their father had abandoned them early. Mother had to raise them mostly on her own. She explained that she had felt guilty for not being around, always working or trying to find work, and felt she had neglected the children who had to fend for themselves most of the time. She had been receiving support from the community, from the church. There was also a support group of parents whose children had disappeared. They shared stories and pooled their tears. Some activists turned up after being in detention, others were just gone. Themba was gone. The police had nothing to say. There were so many different kinds of rumours. Of children used in muti rituals by witchdoctors, of township tsotsis murdering them, of girls in the brothels of Hillbrow in Ho-burg, of MK-Apla-BC camps, and, of course, of death-squads. Rumours of police death squads had begun going around again. A State of Emergency had been proclaimed. Press laws were more stringent. No pictures of police activity were allowed. One had to work constantly vigilant, of everyone and everything. Be creative to get into places, get out of places, to get pics. And people continued to disappear.

Themba was gone. And going out onto the street with a camera held the constant possibility that I was going to commit another kid to death. I went through the motions mechanically. Then, like a godsend, I got an offer to work for an agency in New York, doing picture editing. No going out into the field. An agent with whom I had become close set it up, sensing the condition I was in. Previously, I wouldn't even have given it a thought. It felt like

a betrayal to leave at that time. It was a betrayal. To my friends, to those in the underground to whom I was supplying pictures, to the unseen, unspoken mosaic in which I was a little tile. But I felt my betrayal had come long before. Themba had brought it home to me. Even though I did not take that picture, it seemed like I had done everything else but push the shutter release, and done too little afterwards. It's the kind of betrayal that seeps into you more insidiously, more slowly, I think, but more dangerously. Until the day you start thinking about the nice way the "scarlet red of fresh blood contrasts with black skin," as I had heard one photographer put it. That's the betrayal that settles inside you undetected like a virus, as you begin to think about selling images, winning awards, beating others to the kill. And you only realise it when it's too late. That's the beauty of it. A Faustian pact signed in drunken stupor a long time ago and too late to undo once you've sobered up. In the end your eye becomes an undercover agent for the devil. And you need a fix every day. Or the hangover moves in. Permanently.

Yasmin and I have moved to Manhattan. To a small apartment in the East Village. It is like walking out of your time, of your dimension, into a parallel reality. We have put a distance between us and South Africa, an intimate distance that stands between us and feelings we don't quite know what to do with. At first it felt like being relieved of a backache you thought you were born with. Now I look at images coming in every day. Terrifying images. Sometimes I wish I had been there, to frame it differently, show a different emotion at work in that scene. There is so much in the margins, outside the frame, fighting to get in. Sometimes I wish I had been there not to take it at all. I work with people to whom the local content, the context, the story, individual biographies don't matter. South Africa's images of blood and gore are competing for space on a page with blood and gore from a lot of other places around the world. It just depends on whose blood is in vogue I suppose. Sometimes I glimpse Themba in a crowd of protesters toyi-toying in the images that come in every day. Yet I am scared to admit it. By uttering my hope I would be exposing it to light which would destroy it completely.

Suren Pillay teaches in Politics at the University of the Western Cape. This is his first work of faction. Artwork by the Ramallah Underground (Amer Shomali; Mohanad and Jana). www.ramallahunderground.com

A World Doped on Words

Director Erik Gandini and cinematographer Tarik Saleh's new documentary on the US prison colony, Camp X-Ray and Camp Delta at Guantánamo Bay (affectionately known as "GITMO" to insiders), doesn't ask the difficult questions that one would expect of a hard-hitting exposé. In Gandini's point of view, there's no need to "expose" any of the information that they, as filmmakers, were privy to on their trip to the prison in the spring of 2003. Gandini states that all the information they "expose" is widely available to anyone who cares to cruise the Web: all the sooper-secret documents that appear from time to time on the cinema screen as evidence are available to anyone who cares to explore beyond the sites dedicated to Paris Hilton and Brangelina.

Gandini and Saleh initially travel to Guantánamo Bay in the hopes of obtaining information about Mehdi, a Swedish man being held at GITMO. Mehdi was, according to Gandini, a young Muslim man who felt profoundly disconnected and out of place in Swedish society, although he was raised in Stockholm. When the US began its new war, Mehdi had been living in Pakistan, studying the Qu'ran - this is where he was arrested and subsequently extradited to the prison colony as an enemy combatant.

After the initial footage of Guantánamo Bay, where the filmmakers are unable to obtain any information about specific prisoners, Gandini and Saleh follow up on the now-released Mehdi, whose freedom was brokered by the Swedish government. They interview Mehdi, together with another released inmate, Jamal from England, a man who was imprisoned in Guantánamo at the same time as Mehdi. The filmmakers and Jamal discuss the use of temperature extremes, sleep disruptions, "sexual provocations" and the use of jarring, loud music, played over and over again; Jamal laughingly states that when rap music fails to break him, as it did "the brothers from Saudi and Yemen," they tried Fleetwood Mac and Chris Christofferson.

But while Jamal is talkative, Mehdi remains silent for almost the entirety of the film. Gandini says that when Mehdi was first released, he gave one interview to a journalist, where "he told a lot of stories," and then, he went before his first - and only - press conference in Sweden. Footage of the conference shows reporters bombarding Mehdi with question after question. The manner in which the reporters question Mehdi reproduce, in strange and wondrous ways, the interrogation processes he was subjected to in Guantánamo. One reporter actually questions the believability of Mehdi's reason for being in Pakistan at the time of his capture. Mehdi is initially confused, he does not understand what she is saying. Someone explains to him: "She does not believe you."

I was in the process of writing a paper on Ishtiyaq Shukri's novel, *The Silent Minaret*, when I saw a screening of *GITMO: The New Rules of War* at the Encounters Film Festival at the Victoria and Albert Waterfront theatres in 2006.

Shukri's novel had my attention because it presents invisibility and silence as a possible site of protest. The novel centres on the disappearance of Issa Shamsuddin. Issa's removal from the documenting machinery of the nation state can be seen as an act of insubordination: a means of protesting the categorisation of the colonial body through the map of passports, visas and permits. But reading Issa's disappearance as a site of protest is problematic, since state-organised acts of disappearance are occurring simultaneously as the novel unfolds: the prisoners that Issa sees, on the television screen at the shisha café in London, are the first arrivées in what is to become a notorious system of prison colonies outside official US jurisdiction, outside the legal and physical borders of United States territory. Shukri draws parallels between the ventures of the VOC - the manner in which labouring bodies were moved, removed and erased in order to fulfil colonial desires - and the way in which bodies are similarly disappeared into a global prison archipelago by today's empire, under the guise of the "War on Terror".

I began to see Mehdi's silence, post press conference - and many of the Guantánamo Bay prisoners' reported refusals to cooperate - as a sort of last-resort protest. Silence confuses most of us, who live in a culture where we are told that access to language, information and *speak* are a means of displaying power. Silence, in such a time, becomes an unexpected way of fashioning some semblance of selfhood in the midst of violent loss, a means of maintaining a private self at a time when the harrowing arm of the state attempts to forcibly enter one's innermost physical and emotional being.

When I drove to meet Gandini, I was full of the enthusiasm brought on by the seriousitis that accompanies scholarly work. I couldn't wait to ask him about whether his visit to Cape Town revealed, for him, the parallel trajectories of the two empires. But he puts my agog to rest, once and for all, saying that the woman who works at the front desk at the Hippo Boutique Hotel [in the fashionable Gardens District of Cape Town] didn't know about Guantánamo Bay. He asks me, in the politest fashion possible for a man sporting the clean lines of Milanese fashion, if that level of ignorance "is common here." He wonders if the reason the Desk-Chiquita does not know about the prison colony at Guantánamo is because "South Africa didn't have any citizens there."

In the wake of the 9/11, 2001 attacks, the US opened a prison camp at Guantánamo Bay, Cuba, in January 2002. The hundreds of prisoners therein are not afforded prisoner-of-war statuses according to the Geneva Convention. Instead, they are labelled "unlawful combatants" and have been held without specific charges for indefinite periods of time. According to Human Rights Watch and websites like cageprisoners.com, the number of prisoners is "far higher than the US allege[s]," topping, perhaps over the 1000 mark; the prisoners are mostly there as a result of "extra-judicial kidnappings and extraditions from countries as distant [from the War on Terror] as Bosnia, Malawi and Zambia."

GITMO opens with a phone call made from the snowy landscape of Sweden: Gandini asking a US official if it is possible to visit Guantánamo Bay. It turns out that the answer is a friendly "Yes." Gandini gets in touch with Captain Crosson at Public Affairs, who tells him, with the same unrelenting friendliness, that there are flights out of Puerto Rico (an annexed island off the coast of mainland US territory) just about every week; that the flight from Puerto Rico to Guantánamo Bay is free and that it will cost "$12 a night per person for lodging," plus the cost of meals, telephone calls and internet access. ($12 is about the cost of two "Value Meals" at a McDonalds.) Although one cannot actually go into the prison camp, one can photograph it from outside.

Once the film crew arrives at GITMO, Lt. Moss, the PR guy who takes the media around the base, meets them. Moss' relentless, bug-eyed positivism remains at a high-pitch during the entirety of the tour, highlighting the delights of Guantánamo: the beauty of the beach - replete with soldiers in full fatigues and machine guns guarding the waterfront while unidentified women (perhaps other soldiers off-duty) in bikinis sun themselves on the sand; a 9-hole golf course; and the Morale and Welfare Recreation Centre on Cooper field (where soldiers can play football and baseball). Moss' enthusiasm for the already-present fast food franchises (McDonald's and Subway), and the possibility of the arrival of others (Kentucky Fried Chicken or a Pizza Hut) stress the US Army's care towards soldier-morale.

Moss even introduces the tour bus full of visiting journalists to the wildlife on the base. Gandini tells me that Lt. Moss was proud of the fact that on the US base, iguanas are protected wildlife, while on the rest of the island of Cuba, they are eaten by the Cubans and are therefore endangered as a species. On film, Moss warns the journalists: "Iguanas can be friendly," he says, but "please don't feed them… their friendliness can turn into a bite."

The film follows the paper trail - and the excess of words generated by a war conducted during the era of 24-hour news channels and information overload. It also includes footage of interviews with those in the US responsible for making decisions about the continuation of the prison camps, as well as those used as scapegoats in the fallout following the images of torture released from the Abu Ghraib prison in Iraq - a prison said to mirror the same torture techniques initiated at GITMO.

Some of the most disturbing images are those that are unintentionally revealed: one of the final scenes in the film is a night shot: the prison camp, lit up like a resort hotel. The filmmakers' microphones pick up the screams of the inmates held within, unbeknownst to the PR personnel who have brought them to a spot constructed specifically for the media. Gandini mentions that the Nazis, too, invited visitors to show how well their prisoners were treated in the camps, but that Nazis, like those managing Guantánamo Bay, made similar "mistakes" - unplanned revelations of the engineered horror inside.

The possibility that one could

"disappear" oneself as an act of defiance is profoundly challenging in a culture where resistance is offered by making oneself visible, published, a part of print culture: making oneself visible is inevitable when one enters the public debate of academia; making oneself heard means that one's body becomes part of the documented history of global ventures. But at the same time, the legislative bodies behind powerful nations have historically used documentation and description of individuals to map, regulate and control mobility, a means of isolating people behind ever-encroaching regulatory barriers in order to excise them and remove their ability to engage in the debate surrounding their bodies. Documentation can mean that one is increasingly restricted, as the state tracks one down to remove one from visibility.

Issa Shamsuddin, the character around whose life Ishtiyaq Shukri's novel revolves, is never "present"; however, his disappearance from London, soon after the first images from the War on Terror appear on TV screens, embodies the entire space of the novel. Issa's season of migration to the north ends in an obliteration of presence - a disappearing act. The question, as the book jacket asks,

is whether "his disappearance is a matter of choice - the next step in a journey of self-imposed exile," a final act of defiance - or if his disappearance has been orchestrated by more sinister forces. Shukri never specifies what these "sinister forces" might be, but we, as readers are left with the body of evidence linking his body physical, body political and body historical to a long trajectory of unequal relations between empire and the colonised. We follow the routes of history as Issa maps out his doctoral research; and as voyeurs into portions of his daily life, we, together with him, regard the evidence of history repeating itself on the massive television screen in the shisha café he frequents.

The history that Issa chronicles in his scholarly work - the Dutch East India Company's encroachment into the Cape during the 1600s, and the enormity of the ensuing disruption to human life on a global scale - is superimposed by the current ventures of more familiar global corporations of late modernity: that of US and British corporate interests in Iraq and Afghanistan today. We see, juxtaposed, the formation of the first prison colonies meant to house political dissidents and religious leaders from far-flung outposts of the VOC, and the mirrored prison colonies established in Guantánamo Bay and other unknown, unidentified posts around the world. If bodies were moved, removed and erased in the path of the spice trade of the 16 and 1700s, bodies are equally dispersed and disappeared as collateral damage in the struggle to control the production and distribution of today's weighty commodity. Issa merely recognises the significance of the connection: how the current trajectories of empire follow the blueprint designed by the VOC. He links the creation of a prison colony in South Africa to the modern cells of disappearance created by the US empire - rooted as it is, simultaneously, in the specific locale of US territory, and in dispersed, non-territorial locations in which US corporate interests have positioned themselves.

The problem with reading

disappearance as an act of insubordination against an empire that seeks to document, monitor and immobilise *Minaret's* Issa Shamsuddin is that there are very real state-organised acts of "disappearance" taking place as the novel unfolds. The images that

Issa sees - orange-clad men on their way to Guantánamo Bay - are those of the first arrivées in what later became an intricate system of prison colonies outside the legal and physical borders of United States territory.

In considering the spectacular nature of conducting everyday life during The War on Terror, I wondered what effects the creation of a televised prison colony might have on the consuming public. Why is Guantánamo Bay so visible? Gandini believes that the state regards information as something to be "managed"; and an important goal of information management is the "emotional management" of the viewing public. In bombarding the public with images of Guantánamo Bay, the government also ensures that there is too much information: "It does not mean anything if there is no emotional attachment." He adds, "In the US, crime and punishment plays a very different role; they had to show US citizens that the bad guys are punished."

The US released the first images of "shackled and hooded men from Afghanistan… incarcerated behind barbed wire at the US Naval Station, Guantánamo Bay" in January 2002 (Kaplan). The televised images of the shock and awe bombings of Iraqi cities, together with the constant parade of anonymous, hooded prisoners - whose individual identities are deliberately concealed - reveal the "material and symbolic apparatuses of power," states legal scholar Scott McClintock. And in Camp X-Ray, "as the detainees become less visible, the apparatus of power becomes more visible": the images of the detainees replace the void in power created by the disappeared Towers.

I asked Gandini whether he thought that the images of the paraded prisoners were, indeed, designed to "replace" the symbolic power that the US lost on the day of the attacks on the Twin Towers. He believed, however, that his visit and interviews revealed otherwise.

"Sometimes we think that everything is well-designed; everything has a very smart idea behind it. [But] when you go there, when you meet the structure behind - everything is not like that."
The repeated images of the prisoners in orange garb, Gandini thinks, were "a mistake" on the part of the US Army. "It is a big mistake for the US army to let journalists in. Actually, it was the army itself who released these images. [The Army] has never been successful in replacing these images with others. So the army representatives were complaining, saying: 'That was a very short time in the history of Guantánamo, this is not representative of what is happening now.'"

"When you go there, they give you tapes with new images, like the inmates playing football and stuff like that. Or very anonymous pictures, like the library carriage being pushed through the corridor and the inmates taking books. But these pictures were not distributed as hoped."

I questioned Gandini about what he thinks about the absence of an influential outcry from a host of international political leaders, one that will actually determine changes - although many people, like he and Saleh, are engaged in documenting and protesting the violations of human rights in modern prison colonies. Why no seminal international protests, even as people are being "disappeared" by the machinery of the US army, or as prisoners at Guantánamo Bay commit suicide, thereby fashioning a sort of self-imposed "disappearing act," and effectively removing the authority of the United States Army in constructing and managing their disappearances? Gandini feels that people have been so bombarded with images that they are no longer emotionally connected. He states, "If someone came up to me and said, 'Twenty Guantánamo Bay prisoners killed themselves,' basically escalating and building on the [existing reports of] suicides and torture, still, facts are not going to change things. People have to realise that." He feels film works better: "It works on a much more emotional level."

"What is very successful is that it is *talked* about today; it's over-covered, as they say in media language. So there is the feeling that everything is evolving in the right direction… I have to remind myself that when I hear news about [the prisoners being granted] the status of the Geneva Convention…afterwards, I have to say, 'No that's not true. They have discussed it [but] they have not taken a decision about it… they are willing to grant a *portion* of the Geneva Convention.' This is a very, very, very smart - and unfortunately effective - strategy of keeping the debate alive."

debate kills

Gandini once sat on the panel of a TV show in Sweden, together with the then-foreign affairs minister, Leila Freivalds (who was sacked briefly after). "And [Freivalds] was saying: 'We can't accept Guantánamo Bay,' and 'We are against it.'" Gandini sees her as part of the newspeak: "[If] you've said these things for four years . . . the message I get is that you *can* accept Guantánamo Bay. This very symptomatic of the whole European leadership. I asked her why she and her European colleagues aren't doing something big about Guantánamo Bay. Why do they accept it at all? She replied, 'Yah yah, we discuss it: we are studying the situation.'"

"They are meeting and talking. The message is, 'Let's talk about it.' Four years after the prisoners were first brought in, we are still *talking* about it."

Currently, more than five years into the construction of the prison colony at GITMO, the repetitive newspeak mirrors "something like paranoid behaviour… repeating the same things, saying the same things, but nothing is evolving." And more than five years into the War on Terror, after cases "challenging the legality of [the prisoners'] detention [have been] argued before the US Supreme Court, Guantánamo still appear[s] to many as a strange aberration, an "animal" with "no other like it" as Justice Ginsberg stated. Between 2002 and now, journalists', legal scholars' and human rights workers' accounts of Guantánamo Bay - and Camp X-Ray within - as a "legal black hole, a legal limbo, a prison beyond the law, a permanent United States penal colony floating in another world" have painted it as a lawless aberration. However, one has to keep in mind that Guantánamo is only one island in a global penal archipelago on the list of prison colonies proliferating outside the US, including those in Egypt and countries in the former Soviet Union (Kaplan).

Mehdi was one of few to have their government petition for and cajole their freedom. Gandini thinks that the trauma he underwent is so great that "I thought that the man realised that no matter what he says he cannot be understood; he cannot convey the experience, in fact, into language." Gandini says that he and Saleh realised that language had failed Mehdi, "but he is troubled by emotional trauma . . . I don't think that he would express it the same way as I just did. He's really disillusioned.

After having been at Guantánamo, and after having confronted these words we speak - some of them sort of marketing slogans - he does no longer trust language. It says much about how things work today. If you look at Ché Guevara, he represents actions, not words. If he were alive today, he would see the whole world doped on words."

"We were really hoping to find someone from the inside of Guantánamo who was just good looking and typecasted; a well-spoken and smiling person. That is typical of the media expectation. But you cannot expect that from a prisoner from Guantánamo. These people are marginalised from the very beginning. Mehdi was not even interested in the idea of a Geneva Convention. He was just interested in what God's role was."

Even though Mehdi's father protested daily in a public square of Stockholm, displaying himself in his son's image, locked in a replica of his son's cell (described to be about the size of a king-size mattress, made of mesh and metal), Mehdi was still focused on God's will as the determinant behind his life's trajectory.

Gandini says that when asked about what he thought of what his father did, "Mehdi said, 'Well, I'm happy that he did what he did, but he doesn't have the power. God has the power to get me released.' So we were looking for a very rational truth behind this, according to a lost sense of civilisation or [the possibility of] reconquer[ing] all these words and their meanings, but he's not into that. But at the same time, [we] really understood something about silence; about words vs. silence. Something that we hadn't understood otherwise. Truth, in the end, comes from experiences. They are much deeper than opinions or theses."

The most sinister part of interrogations, especially in isolated islands where no law may reach the human being within, is the removal of privacy - everyday actions, and even everyday thoughts become part of the colony's buzzing knowledge-centre, erasing the possibility of a confidential thought or an individual existence. Camp X-Ray's role in "irradiating and illuminating the opacity of the prisoner[s]' body, subjecting [them] to a regime of truth and visibility," and constant visual inspections removes from them their individual identities: the harrowing interrogations and torture they undergo "represents the disappearance of the body" as "it becomes the medium of the symbolic order of the law" (McClintock).

One of the central tenets of the Geneva Convention for prisoners of war, Gandini stresses, is that "You have the right to answer only four questions." Clips of prisoners from the first Gulf War show pilots who were interrogated in front of cameras repeating the same information: "They kept on repeating: 'My name is… And my ID number is… I'm a sergeant in the US Army.' I think we have really grown up with this idea - that we have this right. And the idea of a right to silence is so strong in American films. So it's such a bizarre thing when you realise that you can lose this right."

He adds, "If you don't understand the value of silence, you probably [understand the value] when you are in Guantánamo Bay, when you have lost this right."

The film ends with a clip of Mehdi placing headphones over his ears, strolling along a wooded area. This footage collides with more newspeak by US spokespersons, press conferences, and the realisation that hundreds more remain - indefinitely - without the right to silence in Guantánamo Bay. These are the new rules of war, the new structures built in aid of the ventures of a new empire. These rules mirror the trajectories of old empires, as Ishtiyaq Shukri's novel reveals. We should know what to do, but yet, we claim to be tied and befuddled by the novelty of the situation.

ON THE WRITERS DESK :

Jayawardane, Neelika. 2007. Disappearing bodies: visibility and erasure, mobility and containment of the third world immigrant during the War on Terror. *Scruitiny2* (forthcoming)

Kaplan, Amy. 2005. Where is Guantánamo? *American Quarterly* 57

McClintock, Scott. 2004. The penal colony: inscription of the subject in literature and law, and detainees as legal non-persons at Camp X-Ray. *Comparative Literature Studies* 41

Shukri, Ishtiyaq. 2005. *The silent minaret.*

chinny peeps — Neelika Jayawardane is a scholar of transnational and postcolonial literature. She is currently based at the Centre for African Studies at the University of Cape Town.

Late

move + reduce red man

I was late and by the time I got to the market square everyone had been herded off to the trains and the trains were leaving - I could tell by the fading whistles and the ochre sky. I felt a pang of something - I'm not sure what - and unburdened myself to the guard. He looked down from under his great helmet and took my jaw in his rough hand. The oddest feeling, wanting to turn and run and also to stay with his holding touch forever.

"Little one," he said, "it's not such a bad thing to be late. I am here because I missed my call-up many years ago. No one from my regiment was heard from again. Besides, there is always another call-up. Some day you will be right on time."

I could say nothing until his hand released me, I could do nothing but feel my tongue fill my mouth, feel how deep in my skull it was planted. What would I say when it came time to speak?

move author

Eric Darton

bleed Red Man —

THE HOLE — *caged*

You sit in solitary confinement stewing in nothingness, not merely your own nothingness but the nothingness of society, others, the world. The lethargy of months that add up to years in a cell, alone, entwines itself about every "physical" activity of the living body and strangles it slowly to death, the horrible decay of truly living death. You no longer do push-ups or other physical exercises in your small cell; you no longer pace the four steps back and forth across your cell. You no longer masturbate; you can call forth no vision of eroticism in any form, and your genitals, like the limbs of your body, function only to keep your body alive.

Time descends in your cell like the lid of a coffin in which you lie and watch as it slowly closes over you. When you neither move nor think in your cell, you are awash in pure nothingness.

Solitary confinement in prison can alter the ontological makeup of a stone.

…

It is hard for me to begin.   Beginnings are like that for me now.

But something happens down there in the hole, something like an event …This event can only occur over a span of years. It cannot take place in time and space the way we ordinarily know them.

Not many prisoners have experienced this event.

…

My body communicates with the cell. We exchange temperatures and air currents, smells and leavings on the floor and walls. I try to keep it clean, to wash away my evidence, for the first year or two, then let it go at that.

…

Memory is arrested in the hole. I think about each remembered thing, study it in detail, over and over. I unite it with others, under headings for how I feel about it.   Finally it changes and begins to tear itself free from facts and joins my imagination.

…

It travels the terrain of time in a pure way, unfettered by what is, reckless of what was, what will become of it. Memory is not enriched by any further experience. It is *deprived* memory, memory deprived of every moment but the isolated body travelling thousands of miles in the confines of my prison cell.

My body plays with my mind; my mind plays with my body; the further I go into the terrain of time, into my memories, the more they enter my imagination. The imagination - bringing this memory into that, and that into this, every possible permutation and combination - replaces further experience, which would, if not enhance it, at least leave it intact.

I remember well, with such clarity. I am blinded by the memory. It is as if I had forgotten - but it is that I remember so well, too well.

…

Every memory has an element of pain or disappointment. It scolds a little and in its own way. These elements are normally overshadowed by a familiarity we can live with - we happily forget the rest. The rest: there is no rest - but a quality we can live with in comfort, a degree of quietude.

In the hole after a while the painful elements begin to throw out shoots and sprouts like brittle weeds in the garden of memory - until finally, after so long, they choke to death everything else in the garden.

You are left with a wild wasteland of scrubby weeds and flinty stone and dusty soil. They call it *psyche-pain*.

It is the same with ideals. Everyone has a few: a touch of idealism, a little passion.   As life in the hole, in the pure terrain of time, continues, your passions are aroused less and less with the help of memories and more and more by your ideals. Love, Hate, Equality, Justice, Freedom, War, Peace, Beauty, Truth - they all eventually become Idols, pure and empty abstract gods that demand your fealty, your undying obedience. Little Hitlers come from every precious feeling, every innocent notion you ever entertained, every thought about yourself, your people, the world - all become so many idols, oblivious to each other, that stridently dictate to you in the prison hole.

don't get near y'self

You cannot fill them up with your days, your years, for they are empty too. But you try - God how you try.

The wasteland that is your memory now comes under the absolute dictatorship of idols too terrible to envision.

...

Don't go near yourself.

Then the mirages in the wasteland. You are far from insanity; you are only living through an experience, an event. The mirages are real reflections of how far you have journeyed into that pure terrain of time. They *are* real.

...

Anything you can experience in the hole, you do to yourself, and after an indecent interval, each occasional experience recalls the old, nice quality of a memory which lies fallow beneath the wasteland. A word in a sentence; a tone in a voice or sound; a fleeting essence in a taste or odor; a momentary texture in a tactile sensation, or a combination of motion and form and color caught by the tail of your visual field. Real things: these are the mirages in the desert.

The real world is out of place in the hole, but the hole is nonetheless there. It is time that no longer moves forward in human experience. You can walk, placing one foot before the other, across eternity in time. All the space you need is six or seven feet. The hole furnishes only that provision: you are living a demonstration of the theory of the infinite within the finite; the dream within the reality.

But the hole is not stuff of dreams, of fantasies: it is all quite real. In fact, it is so real it haunts you.

...

You become silent, contemplative, because you have become inverted. Your sense of perception, having taken in everything, including yourself, within the finite confines of the hole, passes through the monotony and now rises up from the *other side*, the infinite, to haunt you with reality.

...

The mind deprived of experience ... conceives its intellectual faculty to be capable of putting to use a fictional apparatus in the brain. It will believe that somehow it can learn to control this apparatus and use it to move material things, to destroy or change or create physically real things. Shorn of a gracious God, the mind surrenders to Nothing, to Nothingness:

If I concentrated, could I melt the bars of my cell? (Yes. Ommmm). Should I first try to concentrate to move that scrap of dust on the floor? (Yes. Ommmm). Did it move? (I saw it move just a hair.)

The intelligence recedes, no more a tool of learning - because knowledge is based on experience - but a tool of the outside world it is deprived of knowing. It tries to contact other minds by telepathy; it becomes the Ancestor. Words and numbers come to hold mystic significance; they were invented by some arcane magic older than man. The line between the word and the thing vanishes; the intervals of numbers in infinity collapse with infinity.

I do not want to talk anymore.

...

But a kind of genius can come of this deprivation of sensation, of experience. It has been mistaken as naïve intelligence, when in fact it is empty intelligence, pure intelligence. *The composition of the mind is altered.* Its previous cultivation is disintegrated and it has greater access to the *brain, the body*: it is Supersanity.

Learning is turned inside out. You have to start from the top and work your way down. You must study mathematical theory before simple arithmetic; theoretical physics before applied physics; anatomy, you might say, before you can walk.

You have to study philosophy in depth before you can understand the simplest categorical differences assumed in language.

...

You have come full circle; experienced that single event that happens down there in the prison hole. How long does it take? Years. I would say five years or more.

Jack Henry Abbott died in solitary confinement on February 10, 2002. These words, culled from correspondence with the writer Norman Mailer, were written in 1978. Abbott's letters from prison are collected in the book *In the Belly of the Beast*.

IN SEARCH OF YAMBO

Yambo Ouologuem, the Malian author of *Le devoir de violence* (translated as *Bound to Violence*), has not been interviewed in nearly three decades. His doings have been shrouded in mystery ever since he "disappeared" from the West, in effect turning his back on literature. Ouologuem has become an enigma for many, a mysterious figure as well as a highly respected author. Ouologuem's silence is complex and the reasons will, perhaps, never be fully known. It is certain, however, that Ouologuem has blamed the publishers of *Le devoir de violence* for plagiarism controversies that followed the novel's appearance in 1968. In the early seventies, Ouologuem claimed that numerous unauthorized deletions had been made in his manuscript, specifically references to Graham Greene's *It's a Battlefield*, André Schwartz-Bart's *Le dernier des justes*, and other sources. Rather than acknowledging these revisions, the novel's publishers simply disavowed all responsibility and placed the onus entirely upon Ouologuem. Nevertheless, Ouologuem's refusal to write cannot be easily attributed to any ancient grudges he might bear towards the French literary establishment. What complicates matters is Ouologuem's wholehearted return to Islam, the faith of his childhood. In the mid-1970s, Ouologuem returned to Mali, where he is now widely known as a devout marabout. However, even the earlier writings of Ouologuem's "apostate" period cannot be fully understood without reference to Islam, specifically Tidjaniya Sufism as it has historically been practiced throughout West Africa.

During a year's residence at the Université de Ouagadougou in Burkina Faso, I searched for Ouologuem in order to conduct an interview with him. I hoped to better understand his "conversion" to Islam and his rejection of literature. Before leaving the United States, I corresponded with various academics who might know how to reach Ouologuem. Sandra Barkan, who had written an article on Dogon influences in *Bound to Violence*, told me she had heard a rumour that Ouologuem had become an active supporter of a mosque in the Dogon region of Burkina Faso. Others told me they had heard Ouologuem had become an ox farmer and an imam - though nobody knew for sure.

Upon arriving in Ouagadougou, I found Ouologuem's mailing address almost immediately by way of the US Embassy in Ouagadougou. It appeared that Ouologuem lived in the Sévaré-Mopti area of Mali. However, the Cultural Affairs Assistant at the US Embassy in Bamako was not optimistic about my chances of meeting with Ouologuem. A teacher of English at the Lycée de Sévaré, who often met with Ouologuem, had told him that "Yambo's current state of mind may cause him to be reluctant to meeting and talking with people."

By now, I had learned enough about Ouologuem to make me cautious. More than once, I had heard it said that Ouologuem had gone mad. One night, on a bus trip, the mere mention of Ouloguem's name generated passionate argument and controversy among the passengers. Some claimed that Ouologuem was a "great genius" - even the "African Joyce" - while others insisted that he was a "shameful plagiarist" and "madman."

That same week, I had a dream about Ouologuem in which he consented to be interviewed, but he was not happy about it. In fact, he was contemptuous of the whole affair. When I awoke, I told my wife about my dream, but I did little else, for it seemed somehow inevitable that the interview would take place. Rationally, I could not have explained why this was so, but I felt certain something would happen very soon.

My break came during a conference at the University of Ouagadougou on the literatures

FUCKADEMICS
(RAMPS)

OUOLOGUEM

of the Sahel, when I delivered a paper on *Le devoir de violence*. In the audience that day happened to be a French professor, working at the University of Ouagadougou, who had lived in West Africa for some twenty-five years - Professor Nicole Vinciléoni. She was interested in my discussion of Sufi elements in Ouologuem's novel. After my paper, Professor Vinciléoni invited me to dinner at her home. She told me that she liked my paper in one important regard: I had suggested that the conflicting demands of secular and religious life among West African Muslims created a kind of "schizophrenia" and this non-Western form of schizophrenia could be observed in Ouologuem's *Bound to Violence*, only most Occidental critics tended to misread Ouologuem's disassociative (or "esoteric") critique of Islam as a blanket dismissal. Professor Vinciléoni had observed such "schizophrenia," which for her was not a pejorative term but rather an inadequate, Greek word for an experience little known or understood in the Western world.

Since Ouologuem lived in the Mopti-Sévaré area, and since Ouologuem had reputedly become a devout Muslim, possibly even a marabout, she recommended that I get in touch with the main imams at Sévaré. If these men felt that Ouologuem should meet with me, it would be difficult for him to refuse an interview.

Professor Vinciléoni also told me that there lived in Ouagdougou a certain El Hadjj Tall Sékou, a well known local figure and an immediate descendant of El Hadjj Tall Oumar, the Peul conqueror and great Sufi shaykh who had brought Tidjaniya-Islam to the Dogon country - with many prayers and great bloodshed. It was possible that I could secure an introduction to Ouologuem, or at least to the religious leaders of Sévaré, through El Hadjj Tall Sékou. As it turned out, the husband of Ute Fendler, a German friend who

had accompanied me to Professor Vinciléoni's house, Jean-Claude Naba, was well acquainted with the son of Tall Sékou (or "Sékou Tall," as the name would appear in the West). Jean-Claude had once attended school with Tall's son, and could probably introduce me to Tall. He dined with Tall and told him about me. Tall agreed to meet and learn more about my objectives.

In January, Jean-Claude and I drove to Tall's house in one of the older sections of Ouagadougou. After introducing me to Tall's family, Jean-Claude explained that I was editing a book on Yambo Ouologuem, and that I'd like to include a recent interview and other updated, biographical information. We were concerned, however, because of stories we had heard about Ouologuem's strange behaviour. While Jean-Claude spoke, Tall sat back in his chair, patiently stroking his closely cropped head. He was eighty years old, as I had found out from Jean-Claude, though he seemed as healthy as a man in his early sixties. In a country where the life expectancy is less than forty years, I was amazed by his vigour and obvious good health. When I got to know him better, I found out that he had some twenty children between four wives.

"I saw Yambo four years ago," Tall told us. "At the funeral of his father, Boukary. Yambo's father and I were schoolmates in Bandiagara."

"How did he seem?" Jean-Claude asked. "At the time of the funeral?"

"He's fine. He's not crazy like these people say. It's true that Yambo's a quiet man, but he's not mad. In fact, he teaches French at a lycée in Sévaré."

"So he's not mad?" I said.

"No," Tall said. "He's a religious man, a devout man."

"Is it true he's become a marabout?"

"No, he's a militant, like myself. A marabout teaches the Qur'an to children. Yambo is serious about his religion, but he's not a marabout. A militant is not the same thing as a marabout, you see. A marabout has a particular job." In his free hand, Tall clutched a white, intricately woven prayer cap along with a handsome, silver-handled cane. He was a big man with thin, gangly limbs from under his black robe. He decided to accompany me to Mali himself, along with his son Mountaga, so that he could formally greet his older brother, the recently appointed chief of Bandiagara. First, we would attend to the business of meeting Yambo Ouologuem, Tall said, and then we would drive to Bandiagara. What remained now was to work out the details of our journey.

Now that Tall would accompany me, it seemed certain that I would meet Ouologuem. Organising our journey, however, proved to be extraordinarily trying. First, the University of Ouagadougou, where I taught American literature, was currently embroiled in the worst strike of its history. Every day, students were teargassed, beaten, arrested, and even tortured by the Blaise Compaoré government. At times, it seemed that a solution might be reached, and then classes would resume, only to be boycotted a few days later. Second, the feast of Ramadan approached, and Tall did not want to leave until after the celebration. In fact, as a "cadeau" I had brought to Tall a young ram, along with an envelope containing several thousand CFA, for his willingness to accompany me to Mali. This had caused some awkwardness for me, but Tall took it as rightful compensation and seemed content with the amount. Because of the excruciating heat that would come to the Sahel after February, our trip to Mali could not be delayed for long.

Another practical problem was transportation. My own Toyota station wagon worked well within the city of Ouagadougou but it was not made for trips to the bush (as I had found out the hard way). What we needed was a "quatre-quatre" or four-wheel drive, which would no doubt quadruple my costs. However, there was

a friend of mine, an American named Robert Hans, and who was willing to take us in his Cherokee Jeep, but our proposed dates of travel posed some problems for him. Robert, who worked for the World Bank, had already arranged to have dinner with the brother of Blaise Compaoré, to discuss an urgent problem for him - namely, the Burkinabé government was trying to terminate his contract prematurely and force him out of the country.

After much discussion, we were able at last to find a departure date satisfactory for everyone: Friday, 14 February, after Tall's prayers at the mosque. However, it meant a shorter trip than I'd hoped, as Tall insisted on returning by the following Thursday.

The afternoon of St. Valentine's Day, we were finally ready for departure. Besides Tall and his son Mountaga, we had arranged for Robert's driver to accompany us, a Liberian political refugee named James Wade. However, when James had still not finished preparing the Jeep by two o'clock, Robert fumed about the incompetence of his driver, and how Africans in general had no respect for time. Before we even pulled out of Robert's driveway, I questioned the wisdom of my travel arrangements. Robert insisted upon driving the Jeep, a flask of tequila in one hand and a fat cigar in the other. "Come on," he said. "Let's go get your buddy Tall." On his CD system, Mick Jagger belted out "Brown sugar, you make me feel so good," while we weaved in and out of the dirt roads of Ouagadougou. From the back seat, James periodically warned Robert about chuckholes and pedestrians, his hands clutched upon a worn copy of the Bible. "You are a father of four children," James reminded Robert. "Please be careful." And then to me, he confided, "Christopher, can't you see? Robert is not a careful man. He really belongs in the military."

I had never really known anyone from the World Bank before, since both the World Bank and the IMF were banned from most of the conferences I attended and the organisations I belonged to. As we drove to pick up Tall, it occurred to me that I really did not know much about Robert either, except that he had worked for several years in Cameroon and had come to Burkina to help privatise the economy. Now in his mid-to late thirties, Robert was originally from New York City, but he had lived for many years in Miami, Puerto Rico, and Nicaragua. He was

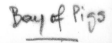
Bay of Pigs

Jewish by birth, though he believed religion in general was a fraud. Our wives had become friendly through the International School of Ouagadougou where our children attended, and we had socialised on a few occasions at school events and children's birthday parties.

Already, Robert was irritated at Sékou Tall because he had delayed our departure until Friday after prayers. It did not help matters when I explained that many Muslims avoided travel on Friday because of the djinn. While fearing the worst, I was astonished when we arrived at Tall's house and Robert began to converse with one of Tall's wives in fluent Fulfulde, a Peul lingua franca he had picked up during his three years in Cameroon. I was even more surprised by how well Tall and Robert got along. Before we had even arrived in Ouahigouya, Robert had developed a real camaraderie with the old man, confiding in him his envy of Muslims - who could have four wives - and his great admiration for Peul women, their remarkable posture in carrying baskets and other objects on their heads. Tall began to jokingly refer to Robert as "le frere de Clinton," after Robert told him he was a Democrat. The old man seemed to admire Robert's incredible energy, even if he warned him about the excesses of his lifestyle. Robert's wife, who was from Bolivia, called him "Vida" (Life), which was an appropriate enough nickname.

Still, Robert did not really seem a happy man, or he at least seemed to be going through a bad time. His efforts to help privatise Burkina's economy had left him frustrated, even embittered. After he had been away for a few years, Africa had somehow lost its lustre for him, and he seemed vaguely bored by it all. Sékou Tall sensed this, and once chanted a little poem, "Robert, Robert, tu as beaucoup souffert."

As we raced over the backroads of Burkina Faso, Robert and Tall shouted at one another over the music of the Grateful Dead, swapping jokes about wives and mothers-in-law. "Let me tell you something," Robert was saying to Tall, "Africa's no place for a white man, especially a New Yorker like me. I don't know why we don't just leave it to all you Africans." This remark seemed to please Tall, who sat enthroned in the passenger seat, his silver handled cane between his knees. Soon, Tall serenely snapped his fingers to Jerry

Garcia's "Truckin'," while Robert played air guitar from the driver's seat. When Robert lit up his foul smelling cigars, Tall answered by spitting his kola nuts onto the floorboards. "So this is American music?" Tall said. "It doesn't sound like Michael Jackson."

The road from Ouagadougou to Ouahigouya is paved, but the rest of the way into Mali can only be passed by the sturdiest of vehicles. Because of our late start, we planned to spend the first night in Ouahigouya, Tall's hometown of sorts, and then we would drive into Sévaré the next morning. As the African bush blurred outside the car window, Tall's son Mountaga explained to me the many complicated alliances wherein his father had come to be heir-apparent to the chiefdom of Bandiagara, as well as the "first Muslim" in Ouahigouya. According to Mountaga, Sékou Tall was the great-grandson of El Hadjj Oumar; grandson of Aguibou Tall, builder of the palace at Bandiagara; and son of Alpha Makí Tall. Mountaga also informed me that the chief at Bandiagara was in reality chief of the entire Dogon people. At first, this seemed confusing to me given the rather obvious fact that Sékou Tall himself was Peul (or "Fulani") and not Dogon. In other words, I could not figure out why a Peul was to be appointed chief of the Dogon people. The more Mountaga spoke, however, I gradually began to realise what I should have known from the start: Tall was himself a descendant of the very "saifs" criticised in Ouologuem's novel, the so-called black Jews who, according to Ouologuem, shamefully exploited the teachings of Islam to oppress the masses of Nakim, or the more "primitive" Dogon.

Later, when I asked Tall if it was true that the Peul were Jews, I saw that my use of the word "Jew" had been indiscreet, acceptable only because I was a foreigner. What Tall preferred to say was that the Peul originally came from Palestine. "It is said that the Peul are a white stream in a land of black water," Tall said, "a black stream in a land of white water." The Dogon people whom I spoke with in Mali did not take such a lyrical view of things, but the mysterious origins of the Peul turned out to be a favourite topic of Tall's, who was obviously proud of his ancestry.

Still, what I had not fully understood before speaking with Mountaga was that Yambo Ouologuem's grandfather, Oumar Karambé Ouologuem - who was of course Dogon - had conspired with the family of El Hadjj Tall Oumar to subdue the Dogon country on behalf of the Peul. In fact, this is how Sékou Tall and Boukary Ouologuem, Yambo's father, had come to be childhood friends. For unlike the vast majority of Malians, Yambo Ouologuem was no lumpenproletariat, or poor subalteran, but rather one of the wealthiest and most highly educated men in Mali. However, if Ouologuem came from an elite, aristocratic caste, I saw now that it was because his family had sided with the Peul in ruling over the Dogon people.

From Sékou Tall, I also learned that Ouologuem came from a long line of Tidjaniya Muslims, the very form of Sufism imported by El Hadjj Tall Oumar. Sékou Tall himself was a practicing Tidjaniya Muslim, though he preferred not to talk about it, except to say that it was dangerous to discuss such things. While Yambo Ouologuem would not have been directly exposed to Sufi teachings as a child - since, as Tall pointed out, Sufi teachings are certainly not matters for children - Yambo's ancestors on both sides of his family were among the most prominent Tidjaniya Muslims in the region. In other words, for Tall, Yambo Ouologuem was in some sense "born" a Tidjaniya Muslim.

The more I learned about Ouologuem's prominent family, the better I understood Tall's earlier insistence that Yambo Ouologuem was no marabout. For Tall, a marabout taught the Qur'an to young children and was supported by his pupils who begged for alms on his behalf. In many Dogon villages today, Mountaga explained, Muslim children as young as four years old commonly leave their parents to follow a marabout for several years, until they have sufficiently mastered the Qur'an. A child's time with a marabout is determined by his ability to recite the Qur'an from memory. In this way, the marabout can devote his life to religion and to the study of the Qur'an. Because Yambo Ouologuem came from a wealthy family, and because he was freed from the necessity of taking on pupils, this disqualified him in Tall's eyes from being a marabout. In Sévaré however, others told me that there were marabouts who did not take on pupils, whose wealth made it possible for them to be freed from this obligation. Despite Tall's reservations, the consensus in Sévaré was that Ouologuem was most definitely a marabout. However, as I was soon to learn, Tall was mistaken about Ouologuem in other ways as well.

When we finally arrived in Sévaré the next afternoon and began to search for Ouologuem in earnest, Tall was clearly astounded at the reports we heard: at the Mosquée Riméibé, an ancient imam named Pâté-Touré who was nearly blind and almost toothless, told us that Ouologuem was indeed a marabout but a very dangerous one, a man who walked the hardest of paths. As the old imam fingered his rosary, Sékou Tall leaned forward in his chair, his mouth agape at the accounts of Ouologuem's doings. As it turned out, Ouologuem not only did not teach at the French school, but his hatred of the French was such that he sent his own children to the Arab-language school in Sévaré. At present, he occupied a government post at a Maison de jeunesse, which required very little of him. This was necessary, the old imam told us, because Yambo did not have many lucid days; in fact, in the eyes of most, Ouologuem was quite mad. Though reluctant to use such terms himself, Pâté-Touré insisted that Yambo's was a special case, a man who had been "touched" by Allah.

The old man told us about the incident when Ouologuem threw rocks at two French tourists who had attempted to photograph the inside of the Mosquée Riméibé. This incident has a quasi-legendary status in Sévaré and we were to hear several different versions of it during our stay. But there were other incidents as well. Not long ago, Ouologuem had provoked a quarrel at the public courthouse, exhibiting such rage that many fled in terror. On the streets, he might approach a Muslim brother and begin expounding upon the most esoteric of questions regarding Qur'anic law, the hadith, dress codes, and other arcane religious matters. While his discourses were often brilliant, he tolerated absolutely no interruptions or contradictions. If his monologues were ever interrupted, he would break off, as if deeply affronted, and then go abruptly about his business.

One incident in particular seemed to bother the old imam. Before prayers one Friday, he had met Ouologuem on his way to the mosque. Under one arm, Yambo had carried a worn edition of the Qur'an. When the old imam extended his right hand in greeting, Ouologuem declined to shake hands, claiming that he had not yet performed his ablutions. In refusing to shake hands, Ouologuem implied that he was unclean, yet his right hand rested upon his Qur'an. For Pâté-Touré no other conclusion was possible:

it was not Yambo Ouologuem who was unclean but he himself. Given the saintly demeanour of the old man, such an inference seemed not only highly insulting but comical. It upset Sékou Tall so much that he got up from his chair and began pacing the room.

"I can only warn you to be cautious," Pâté-Touré said. "There is a precedent. Two other Americans came before you, and Yambo hid himself in the mosque for two days. I wish you the best of luck in your venture, but you must use extreme care. May God's blessing and peace be with you."

We dropped off Sékou Tall and Mountaga at the home of their relatives, while Robert and I took a room at the Hotel Oasis in Sévaré, as it turned out, across from a large piece of property that was owned and managed by Ouologuem. Tall planned on meeting that evening with Ouologuem's uncle, the former mayor of Sévaré, El Hadjj Timbely Oumar, to arrange the introduction. From the hotel patron and his son, I heard more stories about Ouologuem, his religious fervour, his wealthy father, and his eccentric behaviour. The term that I heard repeatedly in connection with Ouologuem was "le fou," or madman, yet all agreed that he was the most highly educated person in Mali, and a truly great man. "They really treated him very badly over there," the patron said. "You see, the French did this to him."

That night, El Hadjj Timbely Oumar came to pay his respects to Sékou Tall, as we all sat in the courtyard of Tall's relatives in Sévaré. Timbely was accompanied by nearly a dozen elegantly dressed men, who encircled him as if part of a royal entourage. Timbely himself wore a white boubou with gold trimming and a white prayer cap. His face was truly remarkable, one of the wisest looking men I'd ever seen. After Tall and Timbely exchanged greetings, Robert and I were introduced. I explained to Timbely that I was editing a collection of essays on his nephew, Yambo Ouologuem, and I'd like to speak with him. I did not want to disturb him, if he truly wished to be left alone, but I wanted to be sure that he was aware of this opportunity to air his views. Timbely listened patiently to my explanation, his hands resting on a sceptre-like cane. At last, he told me that he was happy I'd come, and that in actuality he'd been anticipating my visit.

"I will do what I can to help you," he said, "but you must know that Yambo has not been himself lately, especially since the death of his father," Timbely paused, carefully searching for the right words. "Life has lost its flavour for Yambo. You might say that he has become disgusted with the business of living. He has rejected all things worldly and spends his time reciting the Qur'an and praying. He has even built a small mosque in the courtyard of his house. For a long time, all of us have waited for a change to come to him."

One of Timbely's nephews described Yambo's current state of being. On the streets, Ouologuem at times greeted his friends, but he might just as likely ignore them altogether. One evening, when a group of lycée students, both boys and girls, happened to study together under a streetlight, Ouologuem grew so enraged at the impropriety of this gathering that he grabbed a stick and smashed the streetlight into pieces. He also regularly lectured to the Muslim mothers of Sévaré who allowed their daughters to expose their hair outside their veils, or who wore any kind of decorative mesh. For the second time, I heard a story about Ouologuem's refusal to accept his government pension, much to the chagrin of his family. Because Ouologuem believed the present Malian government and president to be corrupt, he refused to accept any money from them whatsoever.

"After the death of Yambo's father," Timbely added, "we all gathered at the mosque to read the Qur'an. It is customary for the son to make a sacrifice on such occasions, and so Yambo came to the mosque carrying several large books, all written in the Arab language. He wanted us to spend the next few weeks reading these books and studying them with him. We agreed to recite the Qur'an with him, but we refused to even look at the other books. There were so many of them, we would have been reading books for the next two years."

That evening, as friends and relatives described Yambo's behavior, many laughed at his eccentricity, but their laughter seemed indulgent, not ridiculing. If Ouologuem was "fou," he was apparently functioning well enough, living on the inheritance from his father, taking care of his immediate family, and practicing his highly idiosyncratic Islam. When I tried to thank Timbely for helping me, he only shrugged and said that he considered it his duty. Above all, he wanted to help Yambo get over his bitterness. "He speaks often of a certain French publisher, and his years in France," Timbely said. "We are not sure here what happened there, but it was obviously something terrible." I explained the best I could the controversies surrounding *Bound to Violence*, how many had accused Ouologuem of plagiarism. I could see, however, that the details of this controversy did not really interest those present: for most, it was simply another example of French irresponsibility toward Africans, only in this case Yambo was the victim. "The important thing is that you have come," Timbely said. "We will attend to Yambo tomorrow."

During breakfast the next morning, Robert and I discussed what we'd learned so far. As things stood, my fears about bringing Robert along seemed completely unfounded. In fact, he had proven to be a great help, and I felt that I had been unduly prejudiced against him because of his job at the World Bank. That morning, we reviewed Oumar Timbely's plan for meeting Ouologuem. First, Timbely and Sékou Tall would go alone to greet him on the pretext that Tall wanted to express condolences over the death of Yambo's father. (This confused me somewhat since, in Ouagadougou, Tall had originally told me that he had personally attended the funeral of Boukary Ouologuem.) After sufficient time passed, Robert and I would then casually join them and, in the company of Timbely, Tall, and others, Ouologuem would most likely feel obligated to greet us. Timbely also warned us to hide Robert's Cherokee Jeep, which still bore the decals of "Coopération Francaise," the French organisation from which Robert had purchased the vehicle. If Yambo saw the decals and believed we were French, it was certain he would have nothing to do with us.

When we arrived at our predetermined meeting place, a complication arose when it turned out that Ouologuem was not at home but making a tour of Sévaré. Tall and I were content to await his return, but Robert grew frustrated and insisted that we drive to the mosque to find him. "Listen, Tall will sit around here chewing kola nuts all morning," he told me. "Then we'll never get to see the Dogon country. Believe me, it's like this at my office. You've got to push these guys at times, or you'll never get anything done."

We argued the question for awhile, but Tall himself had no objections to Robert's plan, so we all climbed into the Jeep and began searching for Ouologuem.

At last, we found him at the public courthouse, where he had gone to photocopy some old documents. These documents, we learned later, were letters written by some Frenchmen during Mali's colonial period. Ouologuem wanted them preserved in the public archives as a testament to France's crimes in Sévaré. For now, we carefully hid the Jeep behind a tree, while Tall and Timbely approached Ouologuem on the front steps of the courthouse. A few minutes later, Oumar Sow, one of Tall's nephews, motioned for us to come.

Ouologuem never saw our approach because his back faced us, and he was deeply engrossed in conversation with Tall and Timbely. He wore a sky blue boubou with a white scarf, white slippers, and a white prayer cap. His arms dramatically flayed about as he spoke, the packet of letters clutched in one hand. He immediately noted our presence, but did not break off his speech. When Timbely introduced us, he irritably shook our hands but did not allow interruption of the flow of his lecture, an energetic clarification of the different orders of Muslim religious leaders. However, his speech became faster and angrier, his eyes glaringly fastened upon his uncle. As he spoke, I became transfixed by his face, which seemed to me profoundly ugly, not unlike a bust I'd once seen of Socrates, the dog faced philosopher, or perhaps Danton. His cheeks were round and enormous, and they were set in an intense if not bellicose grimace. I lost his train of thought, and only caught up again when he made a heated reference to Judas Iscariot, all the while glowering at his uncle.

Timbely only smiled serenely, and soon we all sat upon metal chairs, brought out by the judge and his secretaries, as Ouologuem continued his discussion of the Muslim laity. I asked him if I could record his voice, but he refused and said, "No, this is not an interview. I came to the courthouse to visit my friends, that is all. Besides, these things can be used against me. I have been exploited before." Nevertheless, his friends repeatedly encouraged him to speak with me, or to at least look at the list of questions I had prepared. In the large circle of his elders and friends, I began to feel sorry for Ouologuem, who had clearly been ambushed by all of us. After awhile, however, he warmed to the idea of being interviewed and even seemed to enjoy the attention he was receiving. He spoke freely on a wide range of subjects, though he never directly answered any of my questions. In fact, he spoke for about three hours altogether. During this time, I listened attentively, wondering how I could possibly remember everything he had said. Later, after going over my notes with Robert, Sékou Tall, and Mountaga, we all agreed upon the basic of what we had heard.

It was difficult, however, to follow Ouologuem's reasoning since his speech was filled with references to his private dreams, prayers, and religious experiences. He also spoke in parables, analogies, and riddles, insisting that the Greek syllogism was vastly inferior to the paradox in its communicative power. His reading in Muslim literature clearly exceeded that of everyone present, who deferred to him entirely in these matters. Often, he built upon a subtle network of allusions from the Qur'an and the hadith, which he seemed to assume - erroneously - was knowledge shared by all those present. Repeatedly he insisted that God speaks through dreams, that the future can be known if we are attentive to our dreams. At times, whenever the subject of French colonialism drifted into his speech, he grew angry all over again, leaning forward in his chair, his voice nearly shouting in rage. His energy was intense, perhaps manic, and when he broke off into a sudden joke, dispelling his previous acrimony, our relief was immense. After one of his jokes, Ouologuem would often slap hands with the judge, with whom he was on very good terms.

Perhaps Ouologuem's most important revelation was that former President Moctar Oul Dada had once offered him a position as Minister of Education in Mauritania, clearly no job for a "fou." Three times Ouologuem had been asked to journey from Mali to Mauritania to completely reform its educational system. The first two times, Ouologuem had refused the offer, leery of the intent of Mauritania's Arab-led government, whose policies towards blacks have historically verged on the genocidal. Given the fact that Mauritania banned slavery as recently as 1980, Ouologuem was rightly cautious about Dada's offer. However, the third time, Ouologuem had been visited at his house by the ambassador of Mauritania in Mali and by Mali's ambassador in Nouakchott. This time, Ouologuem accepted the offer, contingent upon an interim period of several months, so that he might have time for prayer and reflection. However, for reasons that were never clear to me, Ouologuem had not yet assumed this position, apparently as a result of certain political complications that had developed later. The challenges he would confront there would arise chiefly from his desire to synthesise the requirements of a thoroughly modern and yet thoroughly Qur'anic education. He was inclined to accept the position, he told us, because of his desire to end the suffering of his brothers in Mauritania, that is, black Muslims who have historically been oppressed and enslaved by Arab Muslims.

At no point was Ouologuem willing to discuss his writings, and even questions related to literature seemed to irritate him. "I will leave that for you smart ones, the professors," he told me. "I am not a smart man, thanks be to Allah, and smart subjects do not interest me." When I mentioned the name of Wole Soyinka, Ouologuem would not let me finish my sentence. "Another smart one," he said. "An intellectual."

Many of his most hostile remarks were directed at the publishing industry and its many prizes, like the Nobel Prize given to Soyinka. He saw such prizes as a way of controlling African writers and the kind of literature they produced. Ouologuem's criticism, however, was not so much directed against Soyinka as against the publishing industry at large, and the way in which Africa's best minds were routinely exploited by far away presses and the demands of a foreign readership. In his own case, *Bound to Violence* had been published before he'd even signed a contract, and after numerous unauthorised changes had been made on his manuscript. The most famous editorial change was, of course, his editor's deletion of quotation marks in passages later labelled as plagiarised, a fact never denied by his publisher. Ouologuem also claimed that his novel had been translated into English without his consent. If neocolonisation was to be fought, Ouologuem said, the book industry itself would have to be entirely restructured. One place to start was the prize system with its seductive but pernicious cash awards. Ouologuem spoke harshly of Léopold Sédar Senghor, "the most French" of African writers and "a black man who wished that his skin was white."

In fact, one of Ouologuem's greatest fears seemed to be that he would be turned into a "petit Senghor," a Malian curiosity like the mosque at Djenné, or any other tourist attraction. The scorn which Ouologuem heaped upon Senghor echoed a common attitude about the Senegalese throughout the Dogon country. While the Senegalese abused the Dogon as "primitives," the local Dogon (as well as Peul, Malinké and others) ridiculed the Senegalese as French boot-lickers and self-hating blacks. In any event, almost everyone present seemed to share Ouologuem's sentiments about Senghor, or they were at least amused by his rapid-fire monologue. When I asked him his views on the Rushdie affair, Ouologuem refused to comment (as he did with any of my direct questions), but it was clear he had given the matter a great deal of thought. His friend, the judge, seemed particularly upset that Ouologuem would not respond to my question, and he informed us that they had been discussing Salman Rushdie only a day ago. However, Ouologuem steadfastly refused to comment, except to say that his remarks would probably be misunderstood and used against him. In fact, Ouologuem returned to his invective against Senghor and, to the amusement of all, he began to ridicule négritude, especially its reception in the United States. At this point, it dawned on me that Ouologuem believed I was myself an African American in some remote way, a suspicion that was later confirmed when he confided that he had foreseen this visit in a dream.

It was evident that the situation of the African American, especially in the United States, incessantly occupied his attention, and even formed a private obsession with him. He spoke at length of his time in the United States, his appreciation of Malcolm X, his meetings with Cassius Clay, and his participation in the formation of Black Studies programs at several American universities. When Robert asked him which states he visited, Ouologuem again refused to answer directly, but he finally laughed and said, "In any case, I was not in any pious state." Unexpectedly, he blurted out, "You know, we Africans cannot be held accountable for the actions of our brothers over there. This is a fallacy. Many would disagree with me, of course, and I have heard it said that if your goat destroys your neighbour's garden, you are responsible for the damage. Still, these Africans who are causing so much trouble are not Muslims." Like Senghor and all advocates of négritude, he said, blacks in the United States are too obsessed with skin colour. "They have been infected by too many poisonous ideas. In Islam, however, there is no colour." Here, Ouologuem cited two or three hadith wherein it is said that people of all colours are equal in God's eyes.

"Blacks in America must repent," he insisted. "Until they do so, they will continue to live in their own private hell, and this has nothing to do with us in Africa." Here, Ouologuem claimed that his own problem, as well as that of his fellow Malians, was hardly a question of skin color but rather imperialism. With the arrival of the French in Mali, the plight of his fellow Dogon was more closely akin to that of the American Indian, "a new spaghetti Western" in Africa. Above all, he feared that an extraordinarily rich culture, and its many ancient customs, could be destroyed in favour of the most vulgar technological innovations - all in the name of modernisation and progress. Later, I was to learn how serious he was about this when I discovered that, much to the frustration of his wife and mother, Ouologuem refused to allow electricity to be installed at his house in Sévaré. Ouologuem also refused to have his photograph taken by me, citing the biblical injunction against graven images. Timbely, Tall, and everyone present expressed their outrage at Ouologuem's refusal, and even pleaded with him to change his mind. I also reminded him that I had seen a movie theatre across from the Mosquée Riméibé, but he would not budge. The Qur'an tolerated no equivocation on this issue, he said. In fact, this was one of the most defining features of Islam, as opposed to more infidel variants of Ibrahimic religion. As for the movie theatre, this was a fault of the local Muslim community, much to be regretted.

By now, Robert and some of the others had wandered off, and only a few of us remained. As our discussion winded down, Oumar Timbely spoke at length, though he had previously said little. "We are all happy that you have come this far to see Yambo," Timbely said, "and I believe that you will be fair to him, for I can see by your face that you are an honest and just man. That is all we ask, really, that you be fair. Yambo has been treated poorly in the past. He has been exploited and misrepresented. It is only right that he receive justice at last."

At the words of his uncle, Yambo's defiant attitude seemed to dissipate, and he relaxed at last for the first time that morning. He thanked his uncle for his words, while I promised to do my best to be fair to Yambo. In the meantime, my friend Robert had returned, and he was obviously anxious to be on the road. In fact, throughout the interview, Robert had buried himself in a recent issue of *The Economist*, especially during moments in which Ouologuem discussed his private dreams. All of us were disturbed by his behaviour, particularly Ouologuem who did not know what to make of this American - with his short trousers, CD walkman, and two-day beard stubble. Tall also seemed embarrassed on Robert's behalf and attempted to cajole him into their former easy relations, informing everyone that Robert was "le frere de Clinton." Robert was bored, however, and wanted to leave. With a shrug, he disavowed Tall's remark and said, "I can't be Clinton's brother. Clinton's a Christian, and I'm a Jew."

If he had intended to shock everyone, he enjoyed one of his greatest successes. The effect could not have been more jolting if he had suddenly heaved a bucket of human waste upon the gathering. However, there were more surprises in store for us, for in the interim he had instructed his driver to bring the Cherokee Jeep around. When we left together from the courthouse, James stood directly in front of the "Coopération Française" decal until the moment Yambo turned the corner. At that point, James had been told to step aside and reveal the decal. Later, Robert told me that he had merely wanted to "get a rise" out of Ouologuem, to see if he could not "turn Yambo into Rambo." Not surprisingly, Ouologuem was distressed when he saw the French decal, until I was able to assure him that Robert had only purchased his vehicle from the French, and that he was indeed a true American.

Afterwards, we were all exhilarated at our great success. Those who knew Yambo were amazed that he had spoken at such length. Oumar Timbely told me that we had caught Yambo on a good day, when he had been at his absolute best. Our luck had been extraordinary: he had been lucid, funny, sharp witted, and entirely coherent. It was true that there had been moments of great intensity, when we all sensed his stupendous anger, but the presence of Timbely, Tall, and the others seemed to have a calming effect upon him. In retrospect, I questioned the local consensus that Ouologuem was mad, which seemed to me entirely too severe a judgment upon him. Sékou Tall also assured me that, in his own estimation, Ouologuem was no madman. "He's a disappointed man, that much is clear," Tall said. "But he's not any madder than the rest of us." In parting, I left a copy of my interview questions with Oumar Sow, one of Tall's nephews. Mountaga informed me that Yambo would pray about this matter during our journey to Bandiagara. On our return trip through Sévaré, he would decide whether or not to speak with me any further.

When we returned to Sévaré, Tall's oldest nephew walked me over to the house of El Hadjj Timbely Oumar, Ouologuem's uncle. I told Oumar Timbely that Robert could not leave his hotel room because of diarrhoea, the old man smiled with the corner of his eyes. "Did he eat too much?" he asked.

"It's possible," I said. "I don't know. Probably something disagreed with him."

Unexpectedly, James broke out laughing and told everyone it was not the food but the mixture of tequila and beer that Robert had been drinking all afternoon. There was some general merriment at Robert's expense before Tall's relatives, who now seemed content, left me alone with Timbely. In his own house, which seemed like a palace with its complex of buildings, courtyards, and labyrinthine corridors, Timbely's stature was even further enhanced, and I realised now that he was a man of incredible, even extravagant wealth. It happened that an architect was on the premises that day, a white South African, who had spent the afternoon sketching designs of Timbely's dwelling. The architect showed me how Timbely had ingeniously constructed his compound so that he could visit any of his three wives without the others knowing about it. As Timbely and I relaxed in reclining chairs, I could not help but notice the many beautiful women who passed by us, each colourfully dressed in the richest basin fabrics. All wore their hair in long tresses with cowrie shells and other jewellery enmeshed within their intricately woven braids. Soon, Timbely grew irritated at my lack of attention, until I turned my chair away from the courtyard.

Declensions in Blue
— what Silence looks like...

DAVID HAMMONS

MOUSTAPHA DIME

HERVE YOMBI   (mashup by:)
(D. Malaquais)

When a friend stopped by, Timbely introduced me as "the one who had come to bring about the change in Yambo." In fact, Timbely was quite excited about what had transpired in my absence. "Yambo came to see me twice," he said. Timbely repeated the word "twice" as if this was a fact of remarkable significance. "The first time, he was furious that I'd dared to bring a Jew into his presence. He told me that this was unforgivable. But he returned the next day, and he was very happy this time. A great change has come to him at last. He wanted to know when you were coming back. It is certain he will see you again."

Immediately, we sent out James and a nephew of Timbely's to see if Ouologuem would not come by. They had been instructed to tell Yambo that I was leaving in the morning, and that I wanted to say farewell. In the interim, we waited for some time as I translated on behalf of the architect, who had almost no French. We discussed the student strike in Ouagadougou, and President Blaise Compaoré's recent amendment to the Burkinabé constitution [to become Life-President]. As I was to discover shortly, Burkinabé politics were a private obsession of Ouologuem's as well, and it seemed that many in Mali were carefully watching what happened in Burkina. "The trouble with Compaoré is that he wants to be king, not president," I said. Timbely smiled and quoted Abraham Lincoln's aphorism about fooling all the people all the time, which indeed seemed applicable in Compaoré's case: so far, I had yet to meet a single person in Burkina Faso who actually liked or trusted their president. This was perhaps inevitable, given the nature of Compaoré's rise to power, that is, after gunning down the former Burkinabé president, Thomas Sankara, who was still tremendously popular with the people. Our conversation was interrupted, however, when James and Timbely's nephew returned with news of Yambo.

"You must come quick," James said. "He wants you to come to his house." I saw that James was flustered, even radiant, after speaking with Ouologuem. I quickly bid farewell to Timbely, nearly stumbling on my way out, and followed James to Ouologuem's house. James smiled broadly and could not contain his excitement. "I didn't know what your mission was," he said. "Robert told me to stay out of it. It was only tonight that I finally understood. But now I've spoken with Yambo, and I can see that he's a great man, a blessed man." James stopped walking for a moment, and then he exploded in laughter. "But, of course, this guy's completely mad."

"What do you mean?" I said.

"His English is good. This guy speaks better English than people in Liberia. He told me that he wouldn't come to his uncle's house because his uncle is a member of a certain political party in this country that's been exploiting him for the past thirty-three years. He said, 'The reason I don't pay any attention to them is because I consider them to be very insignificant. They think that what they are doing is great, but what they are doing is very simple and worthless, and that's why I don't even question them. They think that I'm a fool, but they are the fools. He's sitting over there calling me. Go and tell Christopher that I'm not going to that house.'"

"Tell me exactly what happened," I said. "What did he say when you approached him?"

"He was coming back from the funeral of some old woman and had been praying all afternoon. When he saw me, he said, 'Where is Christopher's friend? The one with the short trousers?'

"'He's not feeling well,' I told him. 'He has an upset stomach.'"

"Then he said, 'His sins will see him through. He's very insolent.'" (James could not control his laughter at this point.) He stopped and put his hand on my shoulder. "'No, he's only joking around,' I told him. 'He likes to joke. He's not really insolent.'" "'He's a Jew,' he said. 'And you were trying to play smart. I saw you at the car. You went to the car to cover up that sign. What are you trying to hide. Coopération Française? You see, they have bought you. And they reduce you. You have sold your dignity. Just as they have killed Thomas Sankara and taken his body to Wall Street.'"

"He spoke of Sankara?" I asked.

"Yes, he said the body of Thomas Sankara had been taken to Wall Street. So I asked him, 'Why Wall Street? Why not Paris?'"

"'Blaise Compaoré will account for that,' he

said. 'He will explain why they didn't take his body to Paris and instead to Wall Street. Blaise Compaoré will explain that when the time comes. It's just a matter of time. But you Liberians,' he said, 'from the day of your independence, you have been killing one another. And you will continue to kill one another because you have abused your identity. When the Americans realised they were very wicked in dealing with blacks, they decided to export them, to get rid of the rejects. That is what Liberia means. It comes from a Latin word meaning 'the condemned ones,' the ones who were condemned by the whites. They had to find a place for these rejects, and they chose Liberia.'" At this James began to laugh all over again and assure me what a brilliant man Yambo was. "'But the whites made one mistake,' he said. 'They should've left everything with the blacks, but they decided to run things themselves. If they'd done this, today there would be no blacks in America. Instead of giving black Americans the chance to administer their own affairs, they interfered, and today they regret it.'"

"'They got a lot of blacks over in the United States who don't know the direction of their lives, and they are condemned to hell. These blacks say they admire me, they admire my books, but I care nothing for them because they have forgotten their brothers, the suffering masses in Africa. They have sold their dignity. If they really admired me, they would come to Africa and join me for what I have fasted the past ten years, and for what I'm still fasting. I am fasting because I want to see black people everywhere freed from their oppression.'"

By now, we had arrived at Ouologuem's house where I was to hear much of what James told me verified. For the moment, I was too astonished to know how to respond. We knocked at Ouologuem's gate and were greeted by his mother, an ancient, veiled woman who had some trouble with the heavy chains upon the metal posts. The old woman informed us that, unfortunately, Yambo could not speak with us that evening because he was in mourning and occupied with his nightly prayers. We persisted, however, insisting that it was Yambo who had sent for us. "I'm leaving early tomorrow morning," I told her. "I have an important message for him." Finally, she relented and went to get her son. Ouologuem greeted us but refused to shake hands, as

he had already performed his ablutions. Our presence did not seem to make him happy, but his mother offered us chairs while he himself sat upon a huge, felled tree limb. It was completely dark now, except for the light of the moon and stars. Ouologuem's courtyard had a wild, unkempt look with scraggly bushes and vegetation everywhere. We were also introduced to Ouologuem's grandmother, who sat in complete darkness further under the house's awnings.

"I will speak with you tonight at your insistence," he said, "but it would be better if I said nothing." He spoke in English now, and James had been right about his mastery of the language, which was total. "You must know that you are in grave danger," he said. "You and the Liberian are in grave danger here. There are people who would like to kill you. I refused to speak with you because I wanted to protect you. For now, I shall pray for you." From where I sat on a short-legged metal chair, Ouologuem seemed larger than he actually was, his face, scarf, and prayer cap illuminated by moonlight. "It has been four years now since I saw you in a dream," he said, rubbing his eyes. "I dreamed that a Jew would bring a Liberian and an African American." Here, he stopped and looked me over: the fact that I did not seem to be black disturbed him, but only slightly. "These things that I know are hard for you to understand, I realise this. I have the authority to speak the way I want to speak, but if I decide to talk to people like you, I must put things in simpler terms. Still, it would be better if I said nothing at all."

"Silence is always better, you see. This is why I refuse to answer your questions. We speak too much, myself included. Jesus was a silent man. Muhammad was a silent man, too. We forget this with all our books and radios. We drown ourselves in meaningless noise. But if you are able to be silent, you will see that it is much better than speaking." He paused for a moment and placed both hands on his knees. He seemed tired now, as if indeed the effort to speak exhausted him. "I have seen Jesus more than fifty times," he said. "I have spoken with him and with the Prophet. The angels, too, including Gabriel, and they're mostly silent. You must be very careful with people who speak a lot. They think that they know a lot, but they really know nothing." Ouologuem himself fell into silence at this point, as if listening for the sound of the wind blowing through the trees.

It was James who finally spoke. "You are truly a blessed man," he said softly. "God has truly blessed you."

"I am not a blessed man," Yambo insisted. "Far from it. I am simply a man who is seeking God's blessing."

"But you have knowledge," James said, "and knowledge is power."

"No, knowledge is not power. When you are blessed by God, then you acquire wisdom. And when you acquire wisdom, then you have power. Knowledge in itself is not power. You see, God has allowed me to journey to the very frontiers of the human mind. I have seen them unfold before my eyes." With this, Ouologuem swept his hand over his head, urging us to look up at the stars. "The world we live in is truly magnificent," he said. "In Allah, all things are possible if we are only open to them."

There was another long moment of silence, until Ouologuem's mother cleared her throat, signalling for him to dismiss us. "If there's just one message you have," I said quickly, "if there was just one thing you'd like to say to black people in America, what is it?" I am not sure why I asked such a question, but I said the first thing that came to mind.

"Go back to America and tell my black brothers that I've been fasting for the last ten years on their behalf. I've been fasting so that they'll come back to Africa. Tell them to come back to help ease our suffering, and Allah will be merciful. That is the first thing you must say. Then you may tell them that I am now preparing to take over the leadership of the educational system in Mauritania, where blacks suffer more than anywhere on earth. I hope to help establish there a truly Islamic government that will administer to the total affairs of Mauritanians, including Arabs. The worst enemies for blacks right now are racist Arabs, Arabs who have been satanically blessed with oil and who are now funding the Jews and apartheid-type governments everywhere. It is the Arabs who are sponsoring all these organisations that are against blacks, and who invest their money in Switzerland, America, and South Africa. Many have tried to stop me

in this, but I am not so easily defeated. The French have tried to stop me. Even the CIA has offered me a few million dollars. The CIA has already done what it could to me, and they think they have defeated me, but they are mistaken. That is all I have to say."

Ouologuem arose from where he sat, preparing to dismiss us. He again apologised for not shaking our hands and told us that it was time for his evening prayers, that we had detained him long enough. He disappeared into the darkness of his courtyard, and we were led to the gate by his mother. The interview had reached its conclusion.

There were many questions I had for James that night about his long walk with Ouologuem while I waited at Timbely's. Though it had not been possible to record Ouologuem's words, James's short-range memory was excellent - in fact, far better than mine - so I recorded our conversation back at the hotel, as we told Robert about our adventure. Robert was feeling slightly better, though his face was quite pale. When James and I had finished speaking, Robert sat up in his bed and laughed. "Yambo's a nut-case," he said. "A paranoid schizophrenic, and what's worse an anti-Semite. Seriously, the guy could benefit from medication. He might not be able to talk to Jesus all that often, but he could function better." When James repeated that Ouologuem was fine, Robert said, "You don't think he's all that mad because you talk to Jesus all the time. That's the way it is with you religious types."

"Yes," James said simply. "This man is blessed. He said a lot of good things. He's right about blacks in America, too. Africa is the place they come from, but blacks over there don't come and help us. Our brothers in America do not care for us. When we are together, they treat us worse than white men do, as if we are inferior to them. If you look around at all these programs in Africa, the majority of Americans who come are white. Why? With the Peace Corps, even the white ladies are willing to go to the villages and teach our people, but blacks are not willing to come. The problem is that we do not love one another."

"Look it's hard for all Americans here," Robert said. "Things are so different in Africa you don't know what the hell's going on half the time. It's even harder for blacks who have to adjust to this place and then deal with all this bullshit about being 'African Americans.' Most blacks in the US don't have a clue what goes on in Africa. They've got enough problems of their own."

James listened carefully, but he was far from convinced. I remembered then that he had lost a child, and his wife had lost an arm, before they had fled from Liberia as political refugees. Sometime later, James had converted to an anti-Catholic, charismatic form of Christianity, some import from the States. "Okay," James said, "there is truth in what you say, but Yambo is still right. When I was at a refugee camp in Côte d'Ivoire, a brother of Michael Jackson came to sing for us. He came there, and he stood on a bench. Everyone wanted to see this Jackson hero. We were all suffering, and we were glad this guy came to help us. So we listened, and he said, 'You know, I gotta tell you, America is a useless country. America got itself involved in the Middle East thing, in the Gulf War, wasting billions of dollars when they got you here suffering.' So we all looked at one another and said, 'This guy is mad.' There were many highly educated people among the group, some professors, and they too said, 'This guy is mad.' 'You know, when I get back to America,' he said, 'I'm gonna get to Congress and do something for you.'

"I tell you," James said, "we wanted to stone him. This useless guy came, and he made a lot of promises. Then he left, doing nothing."

"What was he supposed to do?" Robert said. "Save Africa all by himself? Believe me, it can't be done. It's not possible. You know, I'm not a religious person, but I believe very strongly that God helps those who help themselves. There are many Jews in the United States like myself who have been very successful. But no one helped me. No one gave me a job or cut me a break. My belief is that countries are successful, and that people prosper or suffer, as a result of their capability to help themselves or not help themselves."

"Yes," said James. "You are right about that. Now you are speaking from the Bible."

Both James and Robert were somewhat surprised when I told them that the saying "God helps those who help themselves" did not come from the Bible but was coined by Benjamin Franklin. Robert in particular was amused by this, which made him feel all the better about being an American. He was currently in the process of securing an entry visa to the US for James, and he was certain that once James arrived in America, he would feel the same way he did.

My search for Yambo Ouologuem had ended. Back in Ouagadougou, I met several more times with Sékou Tall and Mountaga, who both insisted that Ouologuem was no madman. Tall promised to write me a piece for my book, offering his own perspective on Ouologuem's current doings. Mountaga only nodded serenely and said that Yambo was "dur" and that was all. He was one of the "hard ones," not unlike his own father. As for the books Yambo had written some years ago, Mountaga said, these were all literary questions, and so they had of course ceased to interest him.

Ouagadougou, Burkina Faso

8 March 1997

Christopher Wise is the editor of *Yambo Ouologuem: Postcolonial Writer, Islamic Militant,* a collection of takes by Wole Soyinka, Anthony Appiah and others on the life and work of Yambo Ouologuem. Most recently Wise wrote an introduction to the new edition of *Le Devoir de Violence.*

Kneedeepinditchdiggerniggerssweat

His voice had the deep burrr of a man who kept fishhooks
in his beard. So I put on my white muslin jumpsuit, slid
sleeves and levers tight, pulled my hair shut with Sirian
beeswax and en-route superterranean to Toucan Bay via
Antimatic Congo Pump I met Cain waiting with the contraband:
8 grams of uncut Ceboletta X① And while Cain
stroked a reefer the size of Mozambique rolled in a roti
skin, I held my head wide open for the suck with a
nasal>oral siphon and was so oiled and eager for Joe Sam's
return to Houdini's' that night that I sped there, down near
the jetty where fishgutfunk fumed furiously and found
copious peoples rubbing belly to back, hacking heels – knee
deep in ditchdiggerniggerssweat!

That naked island funk was steady lickin' hips with
polyrhythmic thunderclaps! Does the Berta butt boogie? Do
bump hips? Flip'n spin'n bop'n finger pop'n/subaquantum
bass lines pumping pure people-riddim funk like snake
rubber twisting in aluminium bucket, reverberating 'round
the frolic house with a heavy heartbeat, causing black to
buck and shiver –

                    wooeee! wooeee! –

The very groove caused coons to stumble loose and slide
on Saturnalian pomade until their conks collapsed. The
sound possessed more swing than bachelor galvanise in
hurricane, more sting than jab-jab whip, more bone than
gravedigger boots and more soul than African trumpet
bone. It was that pure emotive speed that once improvised
harmolodic funk to Buddy Bolden's punk jazz on the banks
of Lake Pontchartrain, double bass still reverberating
through space-time like long lost Afronauts on orbiting
saxophones. And the solid sound did shook Spiritual
Baptist shacks with rhythm, till the Sankey hymns they
sung became cryptic mantras that slid like secrets through
water.

Up the varnished teak banister, ever afrodizziac in
Indian red, with her high sepia 'fro, far east eyes and
blood
black morello lips borrowed from a jealous mirror,
Madame Sweetbum peeps then leans back on her arse for
support. Puffin' good genk and inspecting vinyl imprints in
dry blue light, releasing slap after slap of the raw boned
and ancient Afrolypso she kept in titanium sleeves –
sacred 45s so sharp rip slippers off feet till steam hisses
from her radiogram. Madame Sweetbum had negroes
wringing brine! Her hi-hat kickin' fat back an' brass,
swingin' – black be boogiefull, black be slick, cryptic
hustlers an' assorted Cyberpimps in stingy brim fedoras,
scissor-tongued vipers in snakeskin brogues, in pleated
pollywool zoot suits with sawed off buckshots in their
lapels. Nubile Supian woman throwing waist like whipsnake,
slip slide/rabid-eyed by stiff crotched coons in erection
boots, leaning at the bar boppin' bulbous foreheads
an' burnin' for flesh.

African

2 WHEELS IN BACK

ONE WHEEL IN F

BACKVIE

① Ceboletta: Dragon blood, spider lily, cocoa onion, Orhid Oncidium, lagrimas de la virgin, Eleutherine Bulbosa (Iridaceae). Cocoa panyols in the valleys of Caura, ancient Tere, worshipped this medicinal plant, nurtured and fed it, cared for it as a child, soaked the ground with blood and milk and planted it at the boundaries of their land. The conqueros used it as a vermifuge (infusion of the underground bulb) for menstrual pain and intestinal disorders. Known to cause genetic flashbacks (phenanthrene derivatives of unknown hallucinogenia). It is said to whistle at night.

Origins of UFO

Meanwhile, Mokotux Charlie climbed the stairs like a
caliper with his clipboard, mop and megaphone. The old
bush coolie ran the place with the rep n'grace of a
gambler's tears. Molasses black with a face like an
unfinished woodcarving, tight brown suit, cockroach killer
boots, white handle razor behind an ear for peeling more
than toe corns and a voice that suggested a rusty trachea.
Charlie liked to grin in that old island pimp style, revealing
ten teeth brown from fifty-five years of Trini pepper, chewing
nush and home-rolled cigars. He also ran severe
érotique noir upstairs where the rooms smelled like dried
pussy, where cum crusted face rags lay under the beds,
where the curtains drooped dank and butter greased while
his ladies charged by the pound; your weight plus theirs in
cash!

Charlie hummed as he shovelled spum from teledildonic
booths and wiped his pros with paraffin. Prime pros
with lineage through ancient ïere; pork-legged jamettes
and melon swallowing domestic cleaner types with devious
profiles, big bone dada mamas whose hips re-tuned
bedsprings to the B flat of authentic colonial brothels.
Some wore names like Yvette, Rose, Daphne and Gemma
who'd just arrived on Kunu Supia from some floating
island behind God's back and she would even let you lick
her mastectomy scar.

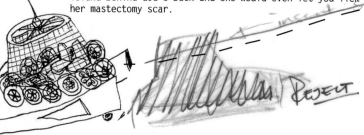

VIEW

But every time the front door swung grown negroes
gaped, glass to lip, sippin'slow, peeping through booze for
Joe. Say say,
"Joe mark to dead, reserve Brandy, salt biscuit, slice
cheese!"
Joe Sam been gone ninety-nine and one half days. No
one no where knew but some speculate, claim say he been
seen hunting giant crustacea in the Kilgode desert, circumpolar
roaming with genetic contraband/he sure to come
back head hard with niggerknots — with a calabash fulla
manjak bitumen between elbows. Soon's his shuttle land
Kunu people go run down from the rainforest to scope Joe
in flesh. Assassins too, go be sharpening they tools, 'cause
all them know one thing for surety: Joe Sam
doh
eat nice!

FRONT VIEW

Anthony Joseph is a poet and a musician. He is the author of two poetry collections: *Desafinado*; *Teragaton*, and a CD
Leggo de Lion with his Afro Caribbean spiritual jazz quintet The Spasm Band. His most recent book is *The African Origins
of UFO*, from which this piece is culled.

N, I figure you are interested in the space theme. It came out of conversations in bars down south with men of the age of Walter (99) debating whether or not man ev
made it to the moon. According to them, and following the Bible's eschatology, man couldn't possibly have been to the moon because Jesus didn't... Ralph then mad
drawings of what a spaceship could look like based on scrap from Walter's backyard. The spaceship was built by Walter's son and a friend. The material included
wheelbarrow wheels, a cart wheel (for the ceiling), the front of a boat (for the body), chicken wire, a fan, lights etc...Ralph also left a book by Samuel Delany on one of
the Spaceship seats. I'll try to get you a pic of that. You also see Walter putting on a spacesuit in the video above the so-called Attic Space. The drawings are also supe
interesting but I don't have good shots of them. Drawings include 60 + notebooks and the Young Baldwin drawings series. The latter based on Little Black Sambo and
The Baby Elephant and a book about (white) children play called What To Do At Recess, mingled with Joseph Beuys and Bruce Nauman impersonations. Also enclosed
painting grid made out of Ralph's 45rpms. C.

installation @
The Kitchen
N.Y.

Spaceship sketches +
video stills from
(The efflorescence of)
Walter
            by Ralph Lemon

    — selected by
        Claire Tancons.

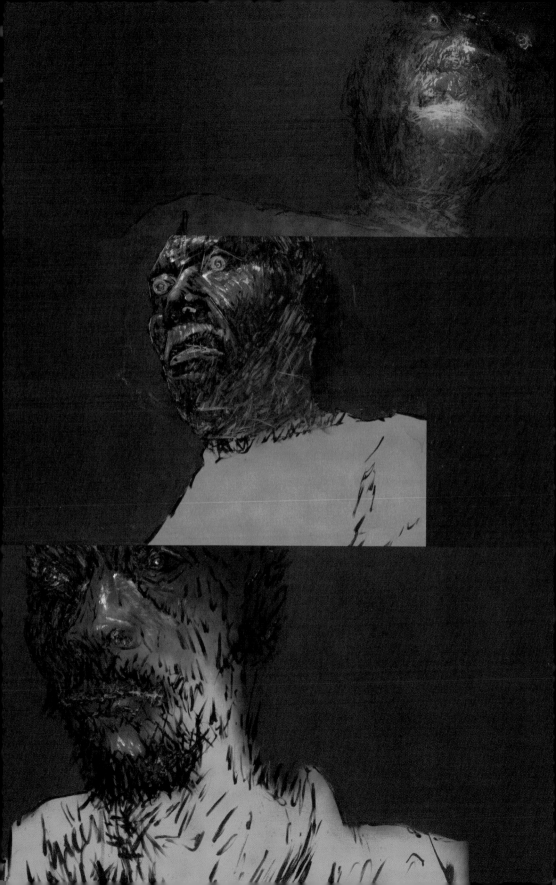

Ruben Um Nyobè, Secretary General of the CPU (Cameroonian Peoples Union), was shot dead on September 13, 1958, in the early afternoon, by French troops dispatched to put an end to a rebellion sweeping the Sanaga-Maritime region since 1955 - a rebellion fomented by the CPU. His death came seconds only after one of his aids, Pierre Yém Mback, was killed. This is how it came about. Men who had started out with Um, but who were now firm allies of the state, told the French - one Captain Agostini, an intelligence officer, and a sidekick of his by the name of Inspector Conan - where to find Um's base camp. At dawn, on Saturday September 13th, several patrols systematically searched Bumnyébel, a small town off the main road linking the cities of Douala and Yaoundé. One of the search parties, which had started off in the village of Libel li Ngoy, was accompanied by local collaborators of the state and by a gaggle of prisoners; among the latter was Esther Ngo Manguèlè, whom the French suspected of being a liaison officer for Um.

Military reinforcements had arrived from Makai. Still others had crossed the Pugè River, on their way from Njok Nkong. The lot of them met up at the base of a hill near Um's camp. First they cordoned off the area; then they set out on a manhunt. *Ralliés* (finks), prisoners and local trackers were made to help. Shortly, one of the trackers turned up traces of the shoes Um was wearing. Aware of the danger he was in, and at the insistence of his entourage, Um had left the camp, probably the night before. His plan had been to move to a new hideout, which Alexandre Mbénd was setting up for him. But the preparations were taking too long, so Um and his companions had decided to lay low in the brush, near a boulder abutting on a swamp. That very morning, Mayi Matip had queried the spirits: nothing bad, he said, was slated to happen today.

Now that it had found the shoe prints, the search party sped up. Within minutes, it located Um's group. Martha, Um's companion on the run, was with him. She was pregnant with his son-to-be, Daniel Ruben Um Nyobè. Um Ngos, the man charged with overseeing Um's base camp, was there too, as well as Pierre Yém Mback, the CPU secretary, Yèmbel Nyébél, the party's administrator, Ruth Poha, Um's mother-in-law, and, of course, Um himself. Immediately, the guns went off. Yém Back was hit first. The soldiers, among them a Chadian conscript called Sara Abdoulaye, were firing in all directions. At first, the trackers had

not recognized Um. Yém fell inches from Um's feet. Um tried to step over a log, so he could shift his body around the boulder and get past the swamp. At that very moment, one of the trackers, Makon ma Bikat, recognised him. Abdoulaye shot Um in the back. He crumbled, dropping as he fell a briefcase containing some documents and several notepads he used to jot down recollections of his dreams. Um moaned and died.

The bodies (among which his mother-in-law's) were dragged to the village of Liyong. They arrived bloody and disfigured. The locals were corralled so they could get a good look at the corpses. The peasants recognised Um and Yém and said so. Ruth Poha's body was left with them. The villagers buried her according to local custom. Um and Yém's corpses became the property of the state. And so they were transported to the town of Eséka.

Yém Mback was buried right away in the Catholic mission cemetery. Um was packed off to the local hospital. There, a doctor by the name of Ntimban examined the corpse - just enough for the necessary papers to be signed attesting to Um's death. Then the body was set up in a large room usually reserved for the ill and dying. In the meantime, the authorities had made up and distributed a tract announcing the death of "He who had turned out to be wrong." Several thousand copies of the tract were printed and passed out in cities and towns all along the railroad line running through southern Cameroon. On the tract was a picture of Um lying dead on the ground. Back at the hospital, Jacques Bitjoka - one of the government's main men - attempted to desecrate the corpse.

He showered it with insults, smacked the dead man's forehead with his right index finger, and defied the corpse to stand up and fight - live up to its reputation, godamnit. Bitjoka would win no matter what. Getting rid of the corpse altogether was impossible. But it was suggested that the head be cut off and the brain removed, for examination. The burial, since one had to happen, was of the kind reserved to reviled men. The families were not invited. Mourning was forbidden. Pastor Song Nlend, of the American Presbytarian mission, held a brief service. The rites to which a man is entitled who has been killed as Um was (*nyémb matjel*) were denied him. No questions were put to the dead man. No meal was held in his honour. No explanations were given. True, he was granted a grave. But, on strict orders from the government, his corpse was first covered in cement; only then was it lowered into the ground.

To understand the sheer weight - the symbolic drama - of Um's burial, it is worth remembering why he was assassinated: for opposing, without ever resorting to compromise, the colonial regime and for refusing to be corrupted as so many were by a government willing to go to any lengths to morally vanquish those who dared rise against it. He had also managed to evade public execution - the lot usually reserved for dissidents (men like Douala Manga Bell and Paul-Martin Samba, put to death publicly in 1914). As he had been a source of disorder during his lifetime, the state decided to use his burial as a means of restoring order. The idea was to abolish, metaphorically, the ruptures, the discontinuities that Um had sought to create in the history of colonial power in Cameroon and, in the process, to show the shining glory of the power he had meant (and succeeded) to disrupt. The very manner of his burial was a play on images of order and disorder, deployed to rob Um's death of the very elements that made it so powerful. The colonial state wanted to shut Um's corpse up. It went about this in several ways.

First, from the forest in which he was killed all the way to the village of Liyong where he was identified by local peasants, the corpse was dragged in the mud. The whole body was disfigured: Um's skin, his head, his hair, his face - all were marred with deep tears. And so Um lost his singularity, the specificity of his features, what made him distinctive - his appearance as a human being. The idea behind disfiguring the corpse was to destroy the individuality of the man, to turn what was left of him into an unrecognizable blob. Then came Bitjoka's insult. This too had its reasons. It had proven impossible to humiliate Um while he was alive, so it was now essential to humiliate him in death, by refusing to grant him the status he deserved - the status that his life, the witness he had borne to his times and the awfulness of his death should have allowed him to claim. For this reason too, he was given but a miserable, anonymous grave. No epitaph, not even a name. As the point was to deny everything that he had been, to erase the very face of him, nothing was to subsist that might allow for the faintest glint of life to live on.

Just to make sure, the body was immersed in concrete. Um's corpse would be allowed no contact with the earth in whose bowels he lay, no physical means to commune with his forebears or, in time, his descendants. The goal, in the end, was to erase Um from the collective memory of humankind, to consign him to chaos and, thus, to nothingness. When independence came in 1960, the freedom Um had fought for so hard fell to a clique that had objected to the very principle of it. This new state saw to it that no means were made available to recall the man or his death.

Determined to drown Um's name in a sea of silence and forgetfulness, the postcolonial state went about disappearing everything he had been (what he had done and written, who he had been in relation to others - every one of those things that had made him the singular being that he was). For a long time after Um's burial it was dangerous to say his name in public, to refer to his teachings, to keep in one's home an effigy of the man or a trace of his writings. Thirty years on, in the late 1980s, Um and his memory were still buried deep under the denial and censorship of the state. Still, his "trace" and his "shadow" perdured, lived on as if phonetically, spoken, written, in spite of the state's insistence that he be forgotten - in spite of an insistence whose very excess, for years, stood as the sole, strident cry of a crime duly admitted. In the very act of forgetting - within an official fable that sought once and for all to do away with him, exiling him deep in the night of those forever unnamed - something of Um had remained.

In the unconscious of this African place that had come to be known as Cameroon, neither his "name" nor the text of his death and burial had disappeared, even as the postcolonial state denied that there *had* been a death or that, for participating in it, it had incurred a debt. "Um": in death, like a grapheme, the name lived on; Um's very name became his testament. In the act of seeking to forget Um, in trying to sink his memory, to say that he was *no thing* - in their desperate quest to purge the country of its recent past - those who had taken over the reins of power showed how irreplaceable the dead man in fact was, how impossible it was to replace his name or the text of which he had been the bearer. For one can only *un*-do what was previously done, remove what once was there.

Achille Mbembe is the author of *On The Postcolony*. These words are excerpted from *La naissance du maquis dans le sud-Cameroun (1920-1960)*, and translated from the French by Dominique Malaquais.

81

El Comandante

(Yousuf) Karsh

June 14

I am thirty-seven years old today. The time has come when I must think about my future as a guerrilla.

Walter baked a cake for us, for me.

June 15

At breakfast Walter told me that he had heard over Voice of America that I am dead. (Walter is insomniac. When he is too tired to read, he lies in the dark and listens to the voices on the shortwave radio.) Last night informed sources murmured of a serious split in the ruling circles of Cuba. Castro has purged me, executed me, as I have executed so many. So end tyrants. Perhaps, reliable sources whisper (and Walter rasps), it was for my criticism of the Soviet trade agreements; perhaps for the failures of my policy of industrialization - it is known that Castro is critical of my "idealistic stand" on moral incentives; or perhaps he and Raul are jealous of my following. Informed sources are uncertain; they had their ears to the door, but the voices were indistinct. The actors emerged and one of the players was gone. A dumb show. They conjectured a plot.

The only certainty is that I am dead.

Fidel Castro, Premier of Cuba, is silent, neither confirming nor denying.

Fidel is silent. The afternoon of our talk, after the ride from the airport in which we each shouted and punched the air, ended in silence, that to some uncanny silence of his, when he joins the world of mineral things; when the most talkative of men, whose life is a stream, river, torrent vapour cloud stream, etc., of words, shuts up; when his gestures, too, his hand reaching out and upward to punctuate a point, to squeeze a shoulder, come to an end. His hands lie open by his sides.

We sat facing each other, neither of us speaking, on the crow's-nest platform he had built in the middle of his room. (To reach it we walked up a circular metal stairway that winds about a thick metal pole. The pole supports the wooden platform.) Fidel sat in a rounded wooden desk chair on rollers (a triumph for someone to have gotten up that ladder), and I made myself comfortable in a small straight-backed wooden chair. We were eight feet off the ground, talking, smoking; not talking. I looked down at his room. His single bed was neatly made, the blue and red blanket tucked tight. (He rarely sleeps here. Uneasy in Havana, he travels all over the island, wandering, in a caravan of jeeps. And in Havana he prefers others' beds.) Iron weights were scattered on the floor, dumbbells, a rowing machine, baseball bats, baseball and boxing gloves, the wide white cross-weave of a trampoline. Fidel does not want to get fat; or old; or die. The trampoline was useless for exercise, though; books were piled all over it. Books were everywhere, books on farming, on soil science, on cattle raising, books on crop hybridisation, books half read, books stacked on the seat of the rowing machine, with red ribbon place-markers sticking out from their pages. Books on the red reclining chair and on the wobbly leopard-skin footrest, books opened and spread face down on the floor, their spines cracking. Scattered about among the wilderness of books were the musical instruments he has tried to play from time to time - a guitar, a bright new brass trumpet, an accordion. (A one-man mariachi band!) For a bad moment I looked about, at the scattered books on agriculture, and the musical instruments he had abandoned (each time he gave up on the project before he had learned to play even a simple tune. Not enough time, not enough patience. There is only one instrument for him: the crowded plaza, his orchestra); and I thought of the factories - my ministry's responsibility - many of them idle or half used, hobbled for lack of raw materials or trained workers, or spare parts. The Revolution was an old engraving I saw once, as a child: a pensive bearded man, a broken god, with a ruined city in the background, a collection of useless instruments around him, a magic square whose impotent charm means nothing beyond itself, a pile of books under his elbow on the spectral unproductive science of alchemy, that promises so much and accomplishes nothing; only one tool: a reaper, instrument of some dubious harvest.

I looked back at Fidel. His eyes were distant, tired. He'd been up the night before, perhaps discussing my arrival, perhaps with a woman. His hands lay on his lap (he'd moved them when I looked away. It made me smile; he didn't respond). He was still now. Immobile. Mineral.

I was exhausted by my plane trip, and would usually have been fretful. I had a clammy smell. But I knew my thoughts. I stretched my legs out and looked at my boots. I put my hands in my lap. I sat.

This silence of his was tactical. (All of Fidel's actions, all his gestures are - or by his genius could later be gathered up into - a tactic.) It was a rare tactic, but not unfamiliar. Occasionally, in committee meetings, in planning sessions (earlier ones, when consent was still often at issue) he would do this immobility business, as if his motor ("the little motor that sets the big motor - the masses - in motion") had run down, finally, for good and all. His hands, which had been busy curling and uncurling the thick hair of his sideburns, fell, as if he'd died, to his sides. His mouth fell open a bit, almost doltishly, if it hadn't been for the intelligence of his eyes, which looked as if they were seeing something puzzling, distasteful. The others chattered on for a bit, until they saw him; then, one by one, they too grew quiet; waited.

His silence was another manner of argument (silence is argument carried on by other means). When he had said all he could think to say (and that meant hours), when he had run out of rhetoric, examples, dialectical twists, and you - a broad, bearded comrade from the mountains, a too-open man - were still obstinate, obdurate, unconvinced, then he would sit like this. You thought the Revolution had promised land to the peasants, land they would own, land they would work themselves. Now Fidel was talking of reserving land for state farms, cooperative enterprises. You glared at those around the table. You were in uniform; some of them wore suit jackets. They weren't comrades; they were shit. No one looked back at you. Fidel's silence meant, "examine your motives"; it meant, "I do not know why you are so obstinate, it's something dark in you that you won't admit to us, perhaps because you haven't admitted it to yourself; some desire for personal power, some petit-bourgeois prejudice; some mulish pride that keeps you attached to your mistake. But I am more obdurate than you. We'll sit here until you discover your error. Or, if you fail, I will end this meeting in silence."

And perhaps you would discover your blindness; or perhaps his silence was (in so many ways) too terrifying to be abided - as if you thought he (or someone) was dying. He, the principle of Revolution, was being absorbed into the nonhuman world. You would do what you must to bring him back, to save him (or someone). You would indeed (and why not call your motive concern, loyalty, love for him whether he was right or wrong?). For perhaps there was, you felt, a glacial change going on within that silence, a change that would be irreversible; a mountain was being gouged from the land by the slow progress of a huge silent mass of ice. You were falling away from him; you were falling down that mountain, out of his confidence. He might smile suddenly and end the meeting. We would get up and leave the high-ceilinged room; and it would be far too late. You would find yourself at a distance from him, in a province, in exile, in jail, dead. His silence prefigured an abandonment, an absence, a death. Maybe yours.

But to revive him now, to bring him back up the chain of being, from rock to man, required a lot of talk from you. You could not anymore simply acquiesce in his plan. You must indicate thoroughly your hidden motive, now discovered, for disagreement. You must show that you had apprehended the flaw in your character, and so seen your theoretical mistake. You must display your understanding of his idea: economies of scale, creation of a new man, destruction of the petit-bourgeois element. You must elaborate for a while on why you now agreed - hard to do, for he had exhausted most of the means of elaboration himself. Perhaps you could use anecdotes from the war: when we had redistributed expropriated cattle to the peasants they had immediately slaughtered and eaten them, afraid the cows would be taken away again. Only state cooperatives could prevent this. I had seen you, a courageous man, drag a wounded comrade from a field strafed by gunfire - but sweat covered your body now as you showed yourself before your comrades. I could smell it: an acrid unpleasant odour. You clasped your fingers together with strain, in prayer, as I had seen you do when you first tried to learn to read. Again, words were failing to come to you. Comrades stared at the light from the high windows, or the discoloured rectangles on the wall where the portraits of Cuba's betrayers had hung. (I, however, watched you perform. You caught my eye and I smiled and nodded. You hated me ever after.) You went on till he spoke, for his silence was a waste of

snow you might have to wander in till your heart froze in confusion and terror.

And often, as the holdout heard himself talk, he found that he now agreed with Fidel, not simply for show, but deeply. (Or was this pride's ruse to save one's dignity?) Even as you nervously spoke (I have been told) you found that something recalcitrant in you had melted. Fidel was right. Of course he was right. Who better could interpret that exacting god, the Revolution? You turned about before our eyes; he had turned you; you wanted even to thank him; you saw things freshly. You didn't feel you had abandoned your position exactly (something you would never have done in a battle, when the enemy was clearly uniformed, when you thought you had known what you were fighting for); rather you simply couldn't find your old position from your new perspective...

But such silence was an extreme tactic for Fidel. He preferred interpretation and reinterpretation, a reworking of everyone's arguments that found opposition to be not opposition at all, but an unsuspected fundamental agreement with him (for the moment), that made you feel that your point was subsumed in his, and that the later working-out of things would join you both (till death do you part).

Or, alas, later some other solution would be found.

Fidel's silence is so powerful because all vitality is in his voice. Once there was...No, this should have a fairytale beginning. Once upon a time there was a CIA plot to damage the Revolution by putting lysergic acid in one of Fidel's cigars. (What appears to them to be a broom is a creature with ears; they have their informed sources, we have ours.) He would smoke the funny cigar before making an important speech to the nation, and become psychotic during the speech, talk all crazy out of his head. This would demoralise the masses.

And there was a dreamlike truth to their idea. Fidel's voice *is* the Cuban Revolution. Not his presence, but his voice. It is as if the island were a narrative of his, a continual improvisation by a master storyteller. He is making them up as we go along; creating characters (was there a proletariat in the way that the revolution required it before he named it, made it know its responsibilities, its power?); and yet one feels at each turn that the story could not be other than it is. He has done this by listening: to hear Fidel speak is to hear a man responding, always; he hears a murmur in the crowd; it becomes a voice inside him; he speaks it; he gives the mass the words it wished but did not know, did not even know that it wished except as an uncertainty, a painful anxiety. The Revolution is the long delirium of Fidel's speeches. Every citizen is a sentence, in that story, as he covers the country with words, makes it out of words, crossing and revising and crisscrossing the island as if it were a giant piece of paper. Fidel gone mad would be the Revolution become farce. They would build big factories to make cookies in the shape of obscene body parts; they would declare war on the Eskimos and load their guns with potatoes and soap; they would dig up sugar cane and plant transistors, waiting patiently for their harvest of radios. And they would become strange to each other, having lost the common term, the common hero, the common language that he is for them. There is no life in Cuba outside the Revolution, outside of his voice. Thus the anxiety when he shuts up.

In the first year of the Revolution, when we still had to make gestures to the national bourgeoisie, and to the North Americans, we made Judge Urrutia the President. He was an old courageous man, a judge under Batista who had voted freedom for the captured men of the *Granma*. But he would not go along with the First Agrarian Reform Law, mild though it was. He accused Communists - myself among them - of subverting the government, misleading Fidel. (For Fidel had made shadows, allowed the national bourgeoisie to believe what it liked about him.) Fidel resigned. The Cabinet tried to meet in his absence; but

nothing could be done without him. Urrutia telephoned Castro and his call was refused. Castro was silent. The Cabinet met again to deal with this crisis; but again they could not agree, they could not calculate his silence, they could not improvise an action. The ministers left the Presidential Palace. Rumours spread. Fidel was silent, neither confirming nor denying. The sugar workers, a union we controlled, called for Urrutia's resignation, that Fidel might be returned to them. The people waited. Was the Revolution at an end? Would Fidel, indefatigable rebel, take arms against the government? That night Fidel spoke on television. He enumerated Urrutia's faults, his mistaken appointments, his too-large house, his too-large salary. "Personally," Fidel said, "I neither have nor want anything. Disinterest is a garment I wear everywhere." What did he need money for if he trusted the people to provide for him? Urrutia was making up the idea of a Communist plot to provoke aggression from the United States. Urrutia planned to flee Cuba, return after the invasion, and run the country for the North Americans. Urrutia made it impossible for him to work, made him impotent, defenceless, exhausted by Urrutia's hysterical anti-Communist declarations that caused international embarrassment and conflict with the good people in the United States. *Urrutia made him silent.* That was what was intolerable. Cuba had found its hero, its epic, this man who spoke in rhythmic cadenced sentences of audacious plans, of future gaiety, of sublime and necessary cruelty, and this gray-haired old man had shut him up, denied them Fidel's voice. Crowds gathered around the Presidential Palace demanding the judge's life. Urrutia fled out the back door. We placed him under house arrest, then let him flee ignominiously to Venezuela. From that time on we ruled Cuba.

I have seen him use his silence as a military tactic too. He would have us wait in ambush, in terrain that we controlled, and watch, watch as the soldiers entered our territory, strung out in a line across a field of tall grass, watch as their bold steps became more hesitant. They had known they were entering our zone, they had steeled themselves for the battle, they had taken the step, the leap, to face the danger, the firing, their death; *why hadn't the firing begun?* They couldn't believe they were safe; how much longer before it began; how much longer would they have to wait? It is terrible to feel in yourself a longing for an attack to begin, a longing for the sight of friends falling around you, perhaps for your own death; so divided, it is difficult to hold your resolve, to hold yourself ready; the line bunched near the front (we always shot the man on point first, so that soon no man would be willing to enter our zone first); you could see the sweat on their faces, under their arms, the terror in their eyes. The silence demoralized them. Then we killed them.

Jay Cantor is a novelist (*Great Neck; Krazy Kat*), and essayist (*The Space Between: Literature and Politics and On Giving Birth to One's Own Mother*). This piece is drawn from his first book, a fictional diary of Ché titled *The Death of Ché Guevara*.

maria

Maria had been standing up for more than a half hour at the bus stop. She was tired of waiting. If it weren't so far, she would have walked. She would have to get used to walking. The bus was getting so expensive. Besides, she was tired and her bag was heavy. The day before, on a Sunday, there had been a party at the boss' house. She had carried the leftovers home - the ham bone and the fruit that had been on the table. She earned the fruit and a tip. The boss was going to throw the ham bone away. Maria was happy in spite of being tired. The tip came at a good time. Her two youngest children were very sick with colds. She had to buy syrup and that medicine to unstuff their noses. The tip would also buy a can of Toddy. The fruits were excellent and there was also melon - the children had never eaten melon. Would they like it?

The palm of one of her hands was hurting. She had cut herself right in the middle when she was cutting the ham for the boss. Unbelievable. The blade cuts to the quick.

When the bus stopped at the corner, Maria reached down and grabbed hold of the sack that was on the ground between her legs. The bus wasn't full, there was room. She could rest a little, take a nap until it was time to get off. When she got on, a man in the back on the last seat got up, making a sign to the fare collector. He passed by in silence, paying his fare and Maria's. She recognised the man. She had missed him for so long. How difficult it was to continue life without him. Maria sat down in the front. The man sat down beside her. She remembered the past. The man lying in bed next to her. Their life in the shack. The

first morning sickness. The enormous belly that everybody said was twins. His happiness. How good. The baby was born. It was a little boy. And he had become a man. Maria saw, without looking, that he was the father of her son. He was just the same. Good looking, big, with a frightened look that didn't fix on anything or anyone. She felt an immense sorrow. Why couldn't it be another way? Why weren't they able to be happy? And the boy, Maria? How is the boy? Do you know that I miss you both? I have an emptiness in my heart, full of nostalgia! I'm all alone. I didn't get by. I didn't want anymore. Do you already have others… other children?

The woman lowered her eyes as if asking for pardon. Yes. She had two more children, but she didn't have somebody else. She stayed from time to time with another man. It was so difficult to be single. And with these sudden affairs, crazy, the two younger children were born. And would you believe it, boys as well? Boys, too? They should have had another life. With them everything should be different. Maria, I didn't forget you. It's all there in this emptiness in my heart.

The man was speaking, but he continued statically, a prisoner, glued to the seat. He whispered the words to Maria, without turning toward her. She knew what the man was saying. He was speaking of pain, of pleasure, of joy, of the child, of life, of death, of farewell. Of the longing in his heart... This time he whispered a little more loudly. She still guessed what he was saying, without hearing him directly: a hug, a kiss, love for the child. And then he got up quickly and pulled

okpundi

Soaked in the gore of expectant cows
five to be exact.
Your crimson shape guarded his temples
from the cheat of his sweat.

Was your smell thicker
than the scent of goat hair
burning at noon?
Or was it heavier
than that of our fathers
during the Biafran war
when they chewed on flesh
and drank their piss
to survive?

out a gun. Somebody else in the back shouted that it was a robbery. Maria was very afraid. Not of the robbers. Not of death. But of life. She had three children. The oldest was eleven and the son of the man who was there in the front with a gun in his hand. The man in the back moved up collecting everything. The driver kept on driving. Everybody on the bus was silent. The voice of the other guy was heard asking passengers to turn over everything quickly. The fear of life in Maria was growing. My God, what would the life of her children be like? This was the first time she had seen a robbery on the bus. She imagined the people's fear. The partner of her ex-man passed by her and didn't ask for anything. And if the robbers had been other men? She would have her bag of fruit to give, a ham bone and a tip of 3000 cruzeiros. She didn't have any watch on her arm. No ring or bracelet on her hands. All she had was a deep cut from a laser-knife which seemed to even cut at life.

The robbers got off quickly. Maria looked nostalgically and despairingly at the first one. It was then that she remembered the anger of the others. Someone shouted that that whore up in front knew the robbers. Maria became frightened. She didn't know any robber. She knew the father of her first child. She knew the man that had been with her and that she still loved so much. She heard a voice. *You black scoundrel! She was in cahoots with the two of them.* Another voice coming from the back of the bus grew louder: *Calm down people! If she was with them, she would have gotten off too.* Someone argued that she hadn't gotten off in order to throw us off the track. She was with the thieves. She was the only one who wasn't robbed. *That's a lie, I wasn't robbed and I don't know why...* Maria looked

in the direction of the voice and saw a little skinny black young man with a baby face who reminded her vaguely of her own son. The first voice, that ignited everyone's anger turned into a shout: *That whore, that shameless black woman was with the thieves.* The owner of the voice stood up and walked toward Maria. She was afraid and angry. What shit! She didn't know any assailant. She didn't owe an explanation to anyone. *Just look at her, still black and bold,* slapping her face. Someone shouted, *Lynch her, lynch her, lynch her!* Some passengers got off and others flew in Maria's direction. The driver had stopped the bus in order to defend the passenger: "Calm down people! What is this craziness? I know this woman by sight. Everyday more or less at this time, she takes the bus with me. She is coming from work, from the struggle of supporting her children." *Lynch her, Lynch her! Lynch her!* Maria was bleeding from the mouth, the nose, and the ears.

Everything happened so fast, so quickly. Maria missed her ex-man. Why were they doing this to her? The man had secreted a hug, a kiss, some love for his son. She needed to get home to give him the message. They were armed with knives that even cut at life. Maria wanted so much to tell her son that his father had sent a hug, a kiss, and love.

The bus was empty when the police arrived. The bag had turned over and the fruits rolled on the ground. Would her children like melon? *Strange fruits*

Conceição Evaristo is a writer living in Rio de Janeiro. She is the author of *Ponciá Vincencio*, a novel, and has published short stories and poetry in *Cadernos Negros*. This story is translated from the Portuguese by Carolyn Richardson Durham.

Chinue peeps

lie — a red hat worn by titled men.

Tell me,
How do you look back at him
while his children sleep?

You, known to
bring him stares
envious ones from rivals
succulent one from village wives
in their heat.

Crowds cheer him into the village square,
watch him take his seat among men
you create.
Their voices hoarse
from carving warriors
out of boys, daily.
Their appetites for food
and sex
flare, the burn of alligator pepper
on young nostrils.

Nwando Mbanugo

My left breast is cool and pale. The right one is shiny and red, a furious apple. The nipple has disappeared, so the baby can't latch when I try to feed him in the front seat of the car. I lift my shirt, but his fists pummel my unyielding flesh. He nuzzles the other side, but it's empty, hasn't filled up since his last unsatisfactory feeding. I jiggle him up and down until he falls asleep to a tenor singing Mahler's *Kindertotenliede* on the sound system. My husband says I must put him back in the car seat, for safety reasons. He reads aloud in snatches from the guide book balanced on the steering wheel.

Covering much of the central Namib Desert and the Naukluft Mountains, the Namib Naukluft Park is home to some of the rarest and weirdest plant and animal species in the world.

I don't want to put the baby back. He'll wake because he's still hungry, and there isn't another car in sight. We haven't passed anything but stones on this ruler-straight road for two hours. My husband will insist though, telling me it's the rule of the road, the law. He's the driver. He'll say he doesn't want to argue with South West Afri… he'll correct himself, Namibian traffic cops. He's not going to languish in foreign jails on account of my refusing to strap the bloody baby in. I want him to stop the car so I can get out and return the baby to the car seat more easily, so I can get a drink from the cooler in the boot. If I ask he'll say he doesn't want to stop unnecessarily, will want to know why I can't just stretch through the seats.

I should try to reason with him. I should say, Ja Liefie, there are many things we don't want to stop unnecessarily, like playing the contrabassoon in the orchestra for the last symphony season. I had to stop. For the baby. Some things we must do for the little ones. The low vibrations of the instrument shook right through my belly to loosen the lining of my womb. I didn't know I was in premature labour. I hadn't wanted to interrupt the maestro in the middle of the symphony concert.

Everything was fine again when I got home and lay on my bed. For a while. I hadn't wanted to disturb the doctor in the middle of the night with my aching back. An aching back is a normal complaint of pregnancy. I'd thought I was imagining things when the weak contractions began twelve weeks early.

I should say, Please stop. He's getting too heavy. It hurts my back to twist and lift.

The baby wakes later and his crying starts my milk again. I lift my shirt and a small spray escapes onto the dashboard. I cover the flow quickly, but it drips on the seat. My husband swerves to a stop, dabbing the dashboard with a handkerchief. "Get out," he says, "I don't want a sticky mess."

My daughter sucks her thumb. "My baby is crying too," she says. "Dolly wants milk. Waah waah waah." The doll, the tenor and the baby chant a bizarre desert counterpoint. Brahms' *Lullaby* would have been a better choice than this lament for all the dead infants of the earth. Poor Mahler, poor Mrs Mahler who lost their child to scarlet fever.

I stand beside the crimson Audi, refusing to cry, kneading my recalcitrant breast, waiting for it to burst and flow. The telephone poles along the road stretch from Helmeringhausen to Sesriem, miles of dust and low thorn bushes. We're travelling through the Maltehöhe region. Our destination is the Duwisib Castle. This morning we left the mineral springs at Eis-Eis.

The mineral springs were rumoured to have healing properties for arthritis, lung complaints and nervous disorders.

Milk from the good breast spurts in a pale arc onto the hot tar, where it turns to steam. I wish it were feeding my boy, but the blockage on the other side won't budge. After a while, the spurting arc turns into a dribble, falling on my shoes. When it dries, it will linger, tacky on my skin. My husband adjusts the volume on the car stereo to drown out the hungry screams.

"Nun will die Sonn' so hell aufgehn…" sings the soloist over marching violins. *Now the sun will rise as brightly as if no misfortune had occurred in the night.*

I steady myself on the wing mirror, holding only the frame so as not to leave fingerprints on the glass. The telephone poles disappear into the pink mountains in one direction and into the desert in the other. How long will my husband wait? He turns the music up a little more. He does that when he's irritated. Once, back at home, before we had children, he got tired of waiting for me, so he drove off without me. I took too long, he said later when I arrived at the party in a taxi.

If he drives away now, will he leave the children with me? Maybe he'll drive off, to scare me, as a joke. If he takes the children, it won't be funny. Will I plod from pole to pole? I press my breast and listen to the voices sparking along the drooping cable.

"Sind Sie dort?" Are you there? "Ich bin nicht hier!" The voices whisper: I am not here. Where are you? There's no one here.

If I can hold out to the castle, there must surely be a hot shower, but if he leaves me, will I crumple and stop breathing, or will I crawl from pole to pole, dragging my nipples through the desert sand?

The telephone poles watch me massage the plug. It must work its way out soon, so that the baby can latch again. I press and press but nothing happens. I twist my nipple hoping to roll the blockage out, wanting to scream at the pain, not wanting to scare my little girl rocking in her car seat, with her fingers in her ears. She also does not like Mahler.

When I get in the car my husband reads aloud from the map:

The Castle lies 1475 m above sea level, and its geographical co-ordinates are 25° 15' 48" South and 16° 32' 40" East.

The whole journey has been an expensive trip undertaken in a bid to get to know each other again. Eight months after my baby's arrival, my husband wants the bedroom back to normal.

"When we get home," he says, "the baby can go on the bottle; he'll sleep in the cot in the next room." I will offer my breasts to my husband instead. He thinks it's a good idea if I go back to work and play in the orchestra again. "It will be nice for you," he says. "It's not a big job, after all, to play the contrabassoon. Mostly you just sit and wait, play a few long notes here and there and go home again afterwards. It will get you out of the house a bit, give you something to do. It's good for a woman to have her own interests," he says.

Dead Vlei is a vast dent of dry, compacted clay dotted with the ghostly figures of ancient camel thorn trees, preserved by the heat and dry air.

The trip is supposed to accomplish all that. We've driven 7000 km hardly speaking to each other - a silence untouched by crying children and the weight of Mahler, punctuated only by comments he has shared from the guide book.

The San people used the milky latex produced by Euphorbias to prepare their poisoned hunting arrows and also to poison water holes.

The noise in my head gathers again, layers of sounds; the low moan of the dunes, a weeping welwitchia mirabilis, the stones on the grumbling hills that mutter and hiss a dark percussion. And always Mahler adding his sorrow. I hope there will be a shower cubicle with a sharp edge where we are going, so I might bang my head under very hot water to drown out the clamour.

We arrive early afternoon. The wind has an icy edge. There is a shower in a vast cool bathroom, but only a feeble trickle emerges from the rattling pipe. My skin is gooseflesh and my nipples contract. I press the thickened spot and massage downward under the tepid water, toward the nipple, like the clinic sister showed me. My hard breast will not ooze a single milky tear.

Last time the duct was blocked, I stood under the shower and massaged my breast, stroking downwards, over and over. The noise in my head got louder, like piccolos warming up, joined by a sax, an oboe and then a hundred violins, each tuning to a different pitch. I had to get the plug out. I turned the water up, hotter, until it scalded my skin. Eventually the blockage burst from my nipple and pinged against the glass door. The release was instant. A solid jet of milk drummed against the tiles and a blue-white swirl flowed down the drain. My head was finally still.

There are no sharp edges to this shower, just a shallow rim of bricks with a plastic curtain that hangs from a sagging rail. I bang my head on the outermost wall, next to the window, on the other side of the bungalow from where my husband minds the babies. I flush the toilet to mask the sound, but the ritual is incomplete and unsatisfying. Without hot water, without the sharp edge, there can be no purge of breast or brain in this alien spot.

My husband calls through the bathroom door, urges me to hurry. The scheduled tour of the castle begins in twenty minutes. We didn't come all this way to miss it. I need a hot compress. If I could only soak a towel and

Hugh
Dubois

icrowave it, but there is no electricity.
 keep forgetting. I look for a hot water
ottle. I could heat a kettle on the gas
lame. Could I put a soaked towel in the
as oven? My throbbing breast must wait until
fter the tour.

The castle was built by Baron Captain Heinrich
on Wolf in 1909," says the tour guide who
as no lips. I stare at the vast chandelier
n the abandoned castle. My husband compares
hat the tour guide says with the notes in
is brochure. "The Baron returned to Dresden
fter the Nama-Herero uprising and married
he step-daughter of the US consul."

The chandelier begins to vibrate. Nobody else
notices. It is the beating of the Baron's
heart that echoes still in the castle's 22
empty rooms. When I ask the tour guide if it
beats from hope or horror, my husband says,
"Now, now, that will do," and asks the tour
guide about the severe oil portraits hanging
on the wall: who was the artist, and when were
they painted?

"The Baron and his wife," says the guide as
we continue into the next room, "commissioned
an architect to build the castle. He wanted
it to reflect his commitment to the German
Military cause. The building materials were
imported from Germany, and travelled 600 km by
ox-wagons after landing at Lüderitz."

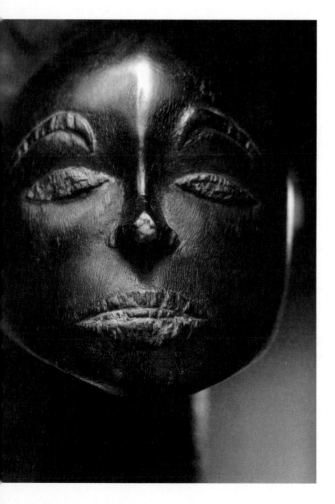

Dubois

My daughter wants to feed the tortoise the Baron left behind. I am scared it will bite off her hand. It is a revengeful giant, sore still from being abandoned. The tour guide says the tortoise is four hundred years old. I watch its ancient eyes. They have a rabid look.

My husband braais under a black sky hung with an infinitude of crystal drops. After dinner we watch shooting stars. My heart beats like the Baron's and I know that one hundred feral horses are galloping toward us both, the Baron and me. The Baron strolls over to our stoep and pulls up a chair, asking us to please excuse his shabby attire. "I've been at war," he says. We drink a Meerlust Cabernet under the stars. It tempers the cold night air. The baby niggles at the good breast. My daughter wants to watch TV. She doesn't like strangers and wants to go inside, to watch Teletubbies or Barney. I explain that TV doesn't work on gas. She wants Smarties. She wants to go home. She cries herself to sleep in a lumpy bed with a scratchy woollen blanket.

I try again after the Baron has left, to help my son to latch on my swollen breast after he's emptied the other one. He cries and cries in the wavering gaslight. I jiggle him on my hip, rubbing my fingers over his gums. I recite the names of the regions of Namibia: Caprivi, Erongo, Hardap, Karas, Okavango, Khomas, Kunene, Ohangwena, Omaheke, Omusati, Oshana, Oshikoto, Otjozondjupa.

The baby has a fever. I knock the bottle of mint-green medicine over in the dark. The spill is sticky in my slippers. I recite the names of the German settlers who left their boldly coloured homes dotted around the desert, with pointed roofs, so the snow wouldn't accumulate on their balconies and turrets. They should have stayed at home with Herr Heckel and Herr Püchner and Herr Mollenhauer who fashioned bocals and bells for bassoons instead.

At 2 am the croup starts. Babies die from that - even back in Jo'burg, at Morningside Clinic, with paediatricians and oxygen tents. I try to boil the kettle over the gas stove, but it makes puny steam. The kitchen is cold. I don't know what to do. I remember the telephone poles and want to call my mother. She would

tell me to keep the baby upright. I sit him in my arms, to keep him from crying, to keep his airways open a little longer. I recite the list of composers who wrote studies for the bassoon: Giampieri, Milde, Orefici, Oubradous, Ozi, Piard, Pivonka, Weissenborn.

The tour guide had spoken in a voice that sounded like snakes winding across the desert, telling of stonemasons from Italy, Switzerland and Ireland, hired to build the castle. Did they leave their wives and babies at home with their violins and tambourines?

The tour guide had said in a voice that sounded like thorn trees rattling in the wind, of how the First World War broke out while the Baron travelled to Europe in 1914. The ship carrying him and his wife was diverted to Rio. Lush Rio, warm Rio, Rio of hot sand and sultry beaches, bananas and guavas, melons and pawpaws. Oh Baron, why didn't you take me with you when you left this barren spot? Come back for me, come back for my babies.

At 3 am I call a doctor 150 km away. I hope he might tell me how to humidify the desert by sprinkling milk on the stars or tears in the dust, but he says, "Jawol, you know that Jayta, the Baron's wife, has found passage to Europe on a Dutch ship, and the Baron is disguised as a woman to avoid arrest. On arrival in Europe, the Baron is scheduled to rejoin the German army."

"So what must I do, Herr Doktor?"

"Keep the baby on the breast and disguise yourself as a man," he says. "I'll see you in the morning at my rooms."

"How will I get there?"

"Make a plan."

At 4 am I call the maestro to ask him to perform the last rites telephonically. He says, "I am occupied on the battlefield of the Somme, giving the last rites to soldiers dying in the mud. The noise inside your head is bothering me."

"There's no sharp edge in this shower and flat walls don't help," I say.

make a plan," he says. "How can I perform
my spiritual duty when you're making such a
din?"

I want to tie my baby on my back and creep
through the dark, over the rocky ground back
to the castle. I want to find the armoire
where the antique weapons are stored but the
baron has returned and blocks the door. He
refuses to let me pass.

"Was wollen Sie?" he asks, ushering me back
to bed.

I want a gun. It seems a good idea under such
difficult circumstances. "Ich brauche ein
Gewehr," I say, unaware I can speak German. I
didn't know the word for 'gun' was 'gewehr'.
Or have I forgotten?

"Haben Sie ein Gewehr?" he asks.

I do not have a gun. He tells me I should do my
wifely duty. I say the trip isn't practical.
Not with a baby and a toddler. We should have
stayed home. The castle could have waited. A
sound begins like a flock of birds landing on
the roof.

"Wife, do your duty."

I tell him it's not practical to play the
contrabassoon any more. The reeds are too
hard, the instrument too heavy. I do not like
to play it. I do not want to perform. The
sound is the rattling *spiccato* of poisoned
arrows shaking in a quiver.

"Put the child down. You must obey."

I tell him the child is sick; I must keep him
upright. The baron finally hears the sound and
says, "My horses, my horses. They're returning
to the stables." But horses don't sound like
pebbles on glass. He crosses to the window
and casts open the curtains. By the starlight
glinting off his buttons and buckle, a many-
armed brown woman enters, riding the tortoise.
She takes off her shoes revealing the feet of
a girl.

At first I think she's a Teutonic Kali, who
will wrap my legs around the Baron's neck
and show me how to bite off his head. I say,

"Kali, Kali, will you lift up my chin and
guide my teeth? I've never done this before.
Please teach me how to drink his blood."

"Hush, hush," says the woman, wiping my brow.
She blows on coals in an ancient pot and
sprinkles herbs that flare and sizzle.

I say, "Kali, Kali, bring me those guns; one
in each hand: for my daughter, for my son; one
in my mouth, one thrust between my legs."

"Hush, hush," says the woman, taking my baby
in two wrinkled old arms. She rocks and holds
him, a hot pack to his chest. A swirl of
eucalyptus scents the room, moistened air
which frizzes his hair.

"Hush, hush," says the woman, as two arms, with
skin neither young nor yet crepey unbutton
my pyjamas. She lifts my red-streaked breast
in one hand, holding a warm poultice to my
burning skin. The air smells of mustard and
bitter yearning. The baby sneezes, saying,
"Bless you."

The many-armed woman slices open the spiked
leaf of an aloe, scrapes its glistening gel
and smears it on my breast. She massages it
down from my armpit in small circular motions,
blowing on the hot spot and talking to the
tortoise; pulling and kneading with her
fingertips until the plug breaks free.

The milk jets onto the hot coals and hisses
a fragrant cloud of steam, "Sie sind nicht
allein." The baby sneezes again, saying,
"Bless you."

Chinopopl

Liesl Jobson plays contrabassoon in the Johannesburg
Philharmonic Orchestra. She received the 2006 Ernst van
Heerden Award for *100 Papers*, her anthology of flash
fiction, which will be published by Botsotso later this year.
Photographs by Hugh Dubois.

Caption somewhere here

Sizzla Kalonji
© Judgement Yard
by Peter Dean Rickards
aka "Afflicted" 1703